ID653406

12 Sept. 1969

INTRODUCTION TO
THE LOWER PLANTS

INTRODUCTION TO THE LOWER PLANTS

F. E. ROUND, Ph.D., D.Sc.

Reader in Phycology, Department of Botany,
Bristol University

LONDON
BUTTERWORTHS

ENGLAND: BUTTERWORTH & CO. (PUBLISHERS) LTD.
                LONDON: 88 Kingsway, W.C.2

AUSTRALIA: BUTTERWORTH & CO. (AUSTRALIA) LTD.
                SYDNEY: 20 Loftus Street
                MELBOURNE: 343 Little Collins Street
                BRISBANE: 240 Queen Street

CANADA: BUTTERWORTH & CO. (CANADA) LTD.
                TORONTO: 14 Curity Avenue, 16

NEW ZEALAND: BUTTERWORTH & CO. (NEW ZEALAND) LTD.
                WELLINGTON: 49/51 Ballance Street
                AUCKLAND: 35 High Street

SOUTH AFRICA: BUTTERWORTH & CO. (SOUTH AFRICA) LTD.
                DURBAN 33/35 Beach Grove

©

Butterworth & Co. (Publishers) Ltd.
1969

Suggested U.D.C. No: 582·2/·3

Printed in Great Britain by
The Camelot Press Ltd., London and Southampton

PREFACE

The 'Lower Plants' encompass a fascinating array of plant forms from morphologically simple unicells through a variety of filamentous organisms to simple leafy structures leading on to the herbaceous but vascular ferns. Beside giant Redwoods and Oaks they may appear relatively insignificant but they colonize much of the available land surface between the more massive Gymnosperms and Angiosperms and extend throughout the aquatic environments which occupy 70 per cent of the global surface. In a world which is rapidly becoming aware of the vital role played by plants in fixing carbon and building this into complex molecules upon which animals are dependent the position of lower plants cannot be underestimated. It has been calculated that the aquatic algae alone probably fix as much carbon as does the land flora but of even greater importance are the activities of bacteria and fungi in decomposing organic remains. These vital processes are themselves not the subject matter of this book but rather it is an attempt briefly to survey structural aspects of the morphology and reproduction of these groups. The author is convinced from lecturing on some of these plant groups that a framework of morphology/reproduction/taxonomy is essential to an understanding of any aspect of their study. The application of modern techniques of electron microscopy, and biochemical and genetic analysis to these aspects of lower plants has added great stimulus to their study. Thirty years ago students may have been forgiven for assuming that some at least of the lower plant groups were worked almost to completion. Today it is obvious that none are and all require intensive restudy of morphology, life history, reproduction, etc. Naturally the examples taken for discussion are some of the better known, but even amongst these there are many basic problems of structure and development still relatively untouched whilst the innumerable other related genera are often only sketchily known. One may ask why this is—the best answer will be provided if you make a thorough investigation of a single lower plant, e.g. a simple liverwort and at the same time list the points you would like the answer to but which are beyond your present scope, such as how many layers has the spore wall, does the germ tube push through randomly, how does it break through, how many cells are formed before the new leafy plant is initiated, how many plants are initiated from one spore, etc. The author hopes that the suggestions for practical work will indicate many such lines of thought and study. Although termed 'Lower Plants' this does not imply 'simple' plants—such do not exist. The biological processes are similar and equally complex in all organisms and when all these processes operate in a single cell then this is as complex as a macroscopic plant in which some of the processes are delegated to certain tissues. The illusion of simplicity is increased by the examination system which often requires study of certain 'types' taken out of their taxonomic context. Whilst these common 'types' are mentioned other related ferns are also discussed and the author has not attempted to simplify the account since this creates an unfortunate false impression of the groups—*Pellia* is not the end of the liverworts!

A grouping such as 'Lower Plants' is of course artificial and merely a convenience for separating off a section of plants for study —in this book they are taken to include all ferns and plants of simpler vascular organization. The book is intended merely as an introduction to these plants, hence references to original works have been omitted since they would in any case be unavailable to the majority of students. Instead suggestions for further reading are given at the end of each chapter and these have been chosen merely to widen the subject matter discussed in the chapter rather than to indicate particular aspects. Illustrations have been completely redrawn and intentionally often simplified and made *semi-diagrammatic*. They should be treated merely as a visual guide to the actual plant structures which whenever time permits should be studied from living material. To this end suggestions for practical study are included at the end of each chapter together with some review questions. Magnifications are not included on the illustrations since in my experience few students use them and indeed without practical experience a magnification quoted as $\times 200$ means very little and with some practical experience such detail is superfluous except in taxonomic works. Most of the illustrations are compounded from many sources and only where they have been obviously redrawn from another authority is this quoted. Nonetheless the author is immensely indebted to earlier workers, particularly to the illustrators of such standard works as Engler and Prantl's volumes of *Die Natürlichen Pflanzenfamilien* and Rabenhorst's *Kryptogamen—Flora*.

F. E. ROUND

CONTENTS

INTRODUCTION

THE diversity of 'lower plants' has long been recognized by biologists who have allocated them to a number of phyla or divisions each of which has a basic series of characteristics. There has been little argument over these divisions, though the modern tendency is to elevate certain classes within divisions to the status of new divisions. Plants which have more complex vegetative and reproductive morphology than the ferns are placed in two divisions—Gymnospermae and Angiospermae. Although the Angiospermae encompass a vast collection of genera they all have certain basic common features, e.g. characteristic meristems, tissues, subdivision into leaves, stems and roots, characteristic male (anthers) and female (ovaries) reproductive organs and associated bracts (petals and sepals). In this sense they are monotonous and hundreds (or thousands) of plants can be picked up and readily allocated to the division without argument. Thus monotony is a characteristic of the division and the same is true of each division of the lower plants except that there is apparently greater plasticity in vegetative morphology though less in reproductive morphology. Applying similar criteria to the lower plants to those used in recognition of the Angiospermae results in a series of divisions which have been familiar to biologists for many years, e.g. Bryophyta (mosses and liverworts) or Chlorophyta (green algae). Fifteen divisions of lower plants were recognized in the 12th edition of Engler's *Syllabus der Pflanzenfamilien*. However, there is certainly no agreement amongst professional biologists as to how many divisions there should be, though my own inclination and that of many phycologists when studying algal groups is that there should be more rather than less. These divisions are, however, collected into the 'Naturalists' old familiar plant groups comprising the mainly unpigmented bacteria/fungi, and three chlorophyll containing groups, algae, mosses/liverworts and club-mosses/horsetails/ferns. The bacteria and fungi are of paramount importance in that they live either on other living organisms or on the dead remains of organisms on the land surface and throughout the seas and freshwaters of the world and everywhere speed up the breakdown of complex organic molecules. Bacteria even occur in the deep trenches of the oceans at depths of over 9000 metres subjected to pressures of 14,000 pounds per square inch! Somewhat larger and more complex are the photosynthetic algae—living in similar habitats but not so extensive since they cannot live or at least metabolize for any length of time in the dark and therefore they do not accompany the bacteria and fungi to any great depths in soil or water. However, in the surface of the soil and in the surface 'film' of the sea they are present as thick swarms of organisms, photosynthesizing so intensely that they rapidly change the balance of oxygen and carbon dioxide and also the concentrations of nutrients. This 'film' is variable in thickness in the aquatic environment, from a metre or so to a hundred metres, but relatively thin compared to the 9000 + metres down to which the bacteria extend. These groups (bacteria/fungi/algae) only rarely form mass vegetation visible to the naked eye, e.g. the algal colonizers of rocky shores. However, in soils and the aquatic environment they form a thick intermingling swarm of organisms filling the space like locusts swarming in the air. Together with protozoa they form the four basic groups around which the discipline of microbiology has evolved. The 'bryophytes' and 'pteridophytes' are relatively much more restricted, occurring almost exclusively on the land surface and although some are adapted to xerophytic habitats they usually form extensive vegetation only in permanently moist situations, e.g. in bogs and in humid 'rain forests'. The 'bryophytes' are small enough to play an important role in colonizing the spaces between the higher plants; natural grassland is a good example to investigate in this respect. 'Pteridophytes' are, however, so large and organized that they have to compete in natural vegetation with the Angiosperms and have the apparent disadvantage of an independent phase, the 'gametophyte', which is often very susceptible to desiccation.

One aspect which adds interest but also complexity to the 'lower plants' is the alternation of generations. The alternation between haploid and diploid states of the nucleus is basic to all organisms undergoing sexual reproduction and is exemplified in its simplest state in algae such as *Fucus* where the vegetative plant is composed of cells all with diploid nuclei and the only haploid nuclei are those found within the eggs and sperm (i.e. as in animals). But this is an unusual state for 'lower plants' which normally form vegetative tissues composed of either haploid cells (known as the gametophyte) or of diploid cells (known as the sporophyte). These tissues may be organized into morphologically similar or indeed identical but independent structures, e.g. green or brown filaments of certain algal genera. Such plants exhibit an *isomorphic* alternation of generations, the haploid plant forming gametes which fuse to form a zygote which germinates into a vegetatively identical but diploid plant. This diploid plant then forms reproductive units during the formation of which a reduction division of the chromosomes in the nuclei occurs and these units then germinate to form the haploid plant. However, the haploid and diploid plants may be quite independent plants, slightly or completely dissimilar, e.g. the seaweed *Laminaria* or a fern plant, and such an alternation is termed *heteromorphic*. In some alternations the one plant remains attached and matures upon the other, e.g. the moss sporophyte (capsule) which grows on the gametophyte (moss plant). Except in that most complex group, the red algae, the sporophyte generation is a single entity, e.g. a fern plant, whereas the gametophyte may be both 'male' and 'female' or either a 'male plant' forming only the male reproductive organs or a 'female plant' forming only the female organs. Fortunately 'male' and 'female' plants are otherwise usually morphologically identical or nearly so, e.g. in the brown alga *Dictyota*.

'Bryophytes' and 'Pteridophytes' have often been grouped together into a loose union, the 'Archegoniatae', since they both possess similar female reproductive structures known as archegonia. However, they also have similar simple sac-like antheridia with a sterile outer layer of cells. Such structures are not confined to these 'lower plants' but extend into the Gymnosperms and it is not the archegonium which is the distinguishing feature but the existence of these reproductive structures on free-living gametophytes. However, even amongst the 'pteridophytes' reduction of the free-living gametophyte can be found, e.g. in *Selaginella* and the aquatic ferns.

In the 'lower' plants the bringing together of two compatible nuclei prior to fusion to form the zygotes is achieved in a bewildering variety of ways—in some fungi no special structures are involved but merely a subtle arrangement of cell walls to separate nuclei of the same parentage and leave together in one terminal cell two nuclei from opposite parents. In other fungi and algae, flagellated gametes of similar or dissimilar size come together and fuse whilst in both groups there is a trend to non-motile egg cells and in some apparently more specialized groups to non-motile male cells. Only in the 'bryophyte' and 'pteridophyte' series can one find comparative uniformity of antheridia and archegonia. Amongst algae and fungi, asexual reproduction by means of motile cells or spores is common and again the range of types is enormous. Only in the formation of the spores produced on the sporophyte after meiosis is there any degree of constancy in the groups—tetraspores, ascospores, basidiospores or the tetrads of the 'archegoniatae'.

Above the algae a very important developmental stage has been intercollated in the life history—this is the embryo and whilst embryonic stages can be distinguished in some algae it is only in the 'bryophytes' and 'pteridophytes' that precise embryogeny can be traced. Such embryos are only precursors of the more complex sporophyte and not of the gametophytes which develop in a more 'algal' manner. This possession of a very distinct embryonic phase has led to yet another classificatory unit—the Embryophyta—which includes all plants of the 'Bryophyte'–'Pteridophyte'–Gymno-sperm–Angiosperm series. It is certainly a most important distinction since the algal/fungal organization has no comparable phase. Obviously a great evolutionary 'jump' occurs between algae and 'bryophytes' although there is a perhaps somewhat lesser 'jump' involved between the relatively simple embryo of the 'bryophytes' and the more complex 'quadrant' types of the 'pteridophytes'.

Vegetative morphology of the 'lower plants' encompasses the range from unicellular through coenocytic, simple filamentous, branched filamentous, thallose to leafy. Three somewhat parallel developments can be traced throughout the groups. First there is the localization of the meristematic cells into certain regions thus enabling greater precision in the growth of the plant. Secondly there is the development of specialized tracts of conducting tissues which can be seen even in some algae, more obviously in 'bryophyta' and most diverse and highly developed in the vascular 'pteri-dophyta'. Thirdly, the expansion of leaf-like photosynthetic laminae culminating in the megaphylls of the ferns is bound up with the development of the branching axis.

All these trends of reproductive and vegetative development and others such as the origin and significance of the position of the sporangia in 'pteridophytes' have been the subject of much speculation and theorizing. Some facets of this will be mentioned in the text but only in passing since the main aim is to review the basic features of the morphology and reproduction of these 'lower plants'.

I

BACTERIA AND BLUE-GREEN ALGAE

THESE two groups form the simplest known lower plants but in spite of this simplicity they are of paramount importance in the economy of the living world. The present-day forms are probably descendants of the most ancient living organisms on the earth's surface. However, even with this long history there is little evidence for the evolution of any other group of plants or animals from them. In some schemes of classification they are termed *monera* or *prokaryotic* plants and are characterized by the presence of deoxyribonucleic acid (DNA) in nucleoplasm unbounded by a membrane. The nucleoplasm itself is not organized into discrete chromosomes although exchange of genetic material has been shown in some bacteria and mutations are commonly found. Many genera are pigmented, but the pigment is not confined to discrete chromatophores. In the blue-green algae there are lamellae in the cytoplasm which in very thin sections under the electron microscope appear similar to those in the chloroplasts of other plants but as with the nuclear material there is no bounding membrane. The cytoplasm of both groups tends to be non-vacuolate and unlike all other plants, mitochondria are absent. The cell wall is composed of hemicellulose, pectin-like compounds or cellulose and mucilage is often secreted to form sheaths around the cells or to diffuse into the medium. The normal method of asexual reproduction is cell division; thick walled spores also form in some species. In neither group is there convincing evidence of sexual reproduction.

Bacteria and blue-green algae are abundant in soils, freshwater and marine habitats as well as colonizing other plants and animals. Only the bacteria cause diseases of plants and animals although certain blue-green algae produce potent toxins which can be poisonous to cattle. The metabolic processes of these plants are of great importance since the by-products are often of value, e.g. the precipitation of sulphur, iron and calcium carbonate, the conversion of nitrogenous compounds and even the extraction of atmospheric nitrogen which is then built into organic molecules. Since they are of such economic importance and also easy to grow at a fast rate they have been used extensively in the study of the molecular transformations involved in metabolism.

Bacteria (Schizophyta)

These small unicellular plants are generally less than 3 μ (3/1000 mm) in length although a few very large forms occur, e.g. the sulphur bacterium *Achromatium* which occurs frequently on sediments in fresh waters and can be as large as 20 μ. Many occur in a unicellular state as spherical (*cocci*), elongate (*bacilli*) or curved cells (*spirilla*) (*Figure 1.1*). If the daughter cells do not separate after division then various colonial types result, e.g. if two coccoid cells remain attached the morphology is termed *diplococcoid*, and if the colony is filamentous it is a *streptococcus* type. Divisions in two planes result in *tetracoccal* forms, whilst divisions in three planes produce cuboidal colonies of the *sarcina* type and irregular divisions produce the *staphylococcus* morphology (*Figure 1.1*). Some bacteria are motile by means of elementary flagella each of which is a microfibril composed of twisted protein chains (a structure quite unlike the $9 + 2$ microfibrils within a flagellar membrane found in other lower plant and animal flagella). They may be either attached singly at one or both ends, or in groups at either or both ends or distributed over the whole cell. Resting cells are formed as endospores within the vegetative cell wall of the bacterium—these spores are often highly resistant to adverse conditions and germinate by a splitting of the spore wall. In *Streptomyces* the spores are cut off from branches of the filaments in conidial-like rows, they are thus exospores. The vegetative cells often secrete mucilaginous capsules containing sugars, e.g. galactose, fructose, glucose, uronic acids and sometimes also amino acids. In addition, toxins (exotoxins) are often secreted through the cell wall; such toxin from *Corynebacterium diphtheriae* causes diphtheria. In some species the toxic compounds are retained within the cell and only released on the breakdown of the cell wall (endotoxins), e.g. that of *Vibrio comma* responsible for cholera.

Bacterial nutrition is extremely varied—autotrophic species obtain their energy from light and inorganic sources (photolithotrophic, e.g. the purple and green sulphur bacteria) or from light and organic sources (photo-organotrophic, e.g. purple non-sulphur bacteria). Photolithotrophy is the common photosynthesis of plants possessing *chlorophyll a* and using water as the hydrogen donor, but although the photolithotrophic bacteria contain a special form of chlorophyll (bacteriochlorophyll—often masked by other pigments) the hydrogen source is never water. Both purple and green sulphur

2

bacteria use hydrogen sulphide as the hydrogen donor and sulphur becomes the by-product in place of oxygen and is stored inside the cells of the purple sulphur bacteria and secreted from the cells of the green sulphur bacteria. The non-sulphur purple bacteria utilize organic molecules from which the hydrogen is removed and combined with carbon dioxide to form carbohydrates—these bacteria are also anaerobic, i.e. metabolize in this manner in oxygen-free environments. However, in the presence of oxygen they tend to behave as chemo-organotrophic bacteria and utilize the organic molecules directly. Chemo-organotrophy is the common method of metabolism of the saprophytic bacteria which decompose dead organic matter and also of the symbiotic and parasitic bacteria which live in other organisms. These saprophytic bacteria occur in all dead organic remains and are vitally important in the breakdown

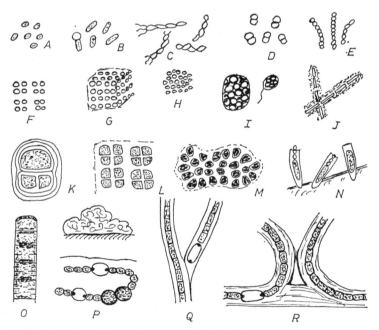

Figure 1.1. Bacteria and Cyanophyta. A, cocci; B, bacilli—one cell with an endospore; C, spirilli; D, diplococci; E, streptococci; F, tetracocci; G, sarcina; H, staphylococci; I, a sulphur bacterium—Achromatium, vegetative amd motile cell; J, iron bacteria—Leptothrix, with iron deposited in the mucilage sheath; K, Chroococcus; L, Merismopedia; M, Microcystis with gas vacuoles; N, Chamaesiphon; O, Oscillatoria, note the new cross walls growing inwards as annuli; P, mucilaginous colony of Nostoc and one filament containing two heterocysts and two akinetes; Q, Tolypothrix, showing branching beneath a heterocyst; R, Scytonema

of dead organisms which would otherwise accumulate since only the bacteria bring about the necessary chemical transformations to simpler molecules and ultimately to H_2O, CO_2, N_2 and thus return these essential elements to the environment for recombination by the autotrophic plants. The requirement of specific organic molecules by many of these bacteria accounts for their specificity to certain hosts and of course they do not require a light source. Equally independent of light are the chemolithotrophic bacteria utilizing inorganic energy sources, e.g. the sulphur bacteria in which hydrogen sulphide or sulphur are combined with oxygen to provide energy and sulphur or sulphate are the respective by-products. Similarly the iron bacteria (e.g. *Leptothrix* and *Crenothrix*) use soluble iron compounds which are converted into insoluble iron, and the hydrogen bacteria which convert molecular hydrogen into water (*Hydrogenomonas*).

Four types of bacteria play vital roles in the nitrogen cycle in nature. One group fix atmospheric nitrogen and thereby increase the nitrogen balance of the soil—these are sometimes species living symbiotically in other plants, e.g. in root nodules of legumes and alder trees where they supply an additional source of nitrogen which the plants incorporate into protein. Others are soil inhabiting species which on decay yield up this fixed nitrogen as ammonia. The nitrifying bacteria operate in the nitrogen cycle by utilizing ammonia ions which they convert into nitrite (nitrite bacteria), which is then excreted to be absorbed by nitrate bacteria which convert the nitrite into nitrate. This nitrate is also excreted but now the nitrogen is in a suitable form for absorption by other plants. Additionally there are bacteria which break down nitrogenous compounds and yield nitrogen which then returns to the atmosphere (denitrifying bacteria).

Another fascinating aspect of some bacteria is the possession of a bioluminescence system, light being emitted as it is by some algae (see p. 42), fire-flies, etc.

Cyanophyta (Myxophyta, Blue-green algae)

This plant group differs from the bacteria in being generally larger, e.g. *Chroococcus* cells may be up to 60–70 μ in diameter, possessing *chlorophyll a* and lamellae dispersed in a pigmented outer region of the cells, undergoing photolithotrophy yielding oxygen as a by-product and possessing two pigments characteristic of the group, C-phycocyanin and C-phycoerythrin. Another striking feature of the blue-green algae is the absence of any flagellate stages

—thus in this feature the bacteria are better endowed since some at least have simple flagellae. Sexual stages are unknown and one can be certain that no elaborate sexual mechanisms are present since blue-green algae have been widely studied for many decades both in nature and in culture. It cannot be concluded, however, that there is no exchange of genetic material until more extensive studies are undertaken.

Cyanophyta are extremely abundant algae and many people see them without recognizing their true nature, e.g. they often form blackish jelly-like masses on garden paths and bluish-black films on plant pots in moist greenhouses and even down the concrete sides of buildings, especially in humid tropical regions. They are abundant on soils where in relatively undisturbed situations they form small circular blackish patches, whilst in moist tropical regions a similar flora extends up tree trunks and on to the leaf surfaces. In aquatic habitats they exist in the free floating phytoplankton and as epiphytes on water plants, sometimes on animals and also free-living on the underwater sediments. Their great degree of tolerance to environmental conditions enables them to live in hot, sulphur springs and they can probably tolerate higher temperatures than any other plant group.

With a little experience these algae are easily recognizable. As mentioned above they are often not blue-green in colour, especially when seen *en masse*, and owing to the presence of a large number of pigments and especially the blue and red phycobilins the resulting coloration can vary from greyish through yellow, green, blue, red and even black. The latter colour is often caused by gas vacuoles in the cells. The presence of these gas vacuoles is linked with the ability of some species to fix atmospheric nitrogen. Apart from recognition by colour, and in the many that are truly blue-green this is not difficult, there are also the negative characters of absence of nucleus and plastids. Small granules may occur in the cells, some of these being the reserve product known as cyanophycean-starch—a starch-like polymer of unknown chemical composition.

As in bacteria, copious production of mucilage often results in cells or filaments buried in a jelly-like mass—look for *Nostoc* colonies on well trodden paths and this will be obvious. Morphologically they show a similar range to the bacteria—unicells, however, are rare for even in the simplest types the daughter cells tend to remain together to form characteristically-shaped colonies, e.g. *Chroococcus* which is common on the sediment of bog pools and *Microcystis* (*Figure 1.1*) commonly found floating in small productive lakes. Flat plates of cells occur, e.g. *Merismopedia*, and also cubical colonies, e.g. *Eucapsis*. An attached freshwater unicell is *Chamaesiphon* which produces a vase-like wall around itself and also reproduces by the formation of exospores. The commonest morphology, however, is that of a filament, often unbranched, e.g. *Nostoc* and *Oscillatoria*, but sometimes branching by simple splitting of the filament followed by extrusion of the ends through the parent sheath, e.g. *Scytonema*, or by a similar pushing out beneath the special spore known as a heterocyst, e.g. *Tolypothrix* (*Figure 1.1*). Heterocysts are confined to certain families of filamentous blue-green algae and they are apparently empty cells with a plug at one or both ends—very detailed investigation has shown, however, that they contain some cytoplasm and can germinate to form new filaments. Sometimes the heterocysts are formed adjacent to enlarged cells with dense contents. These are also spores known as akinetes and form a survival spore.

Surprisingly very many blue-green algae are actively motile and this is presumed to be motivated by some form of gliding, either within the mucilage sheaths or by a 'snail-like' movement, of the whole filament. Some filamentous genera produce more actively motile segments of the thallus known as hormogonia and these act as vegetative reproductive units.

The blue-green algae undoubtedly play an important role as producers of organic matter in soils and aquatic habitats and when this is coupled with atmospheric nitrogen fixation they actually act as nitrogenous fertilizers. Unlike the bacteria they are not serious parasites though some colourless forms occur in animals—these are, however, difficult to distinguish from bacteria—and some are symbiotic with other plants, e.g. lichens (see p. 92), the liverwort *Anthoceros*, the Cycad, *Cycas*, and the Angiosperm, *Gunnera*.

Classification

The bacteria are separated from the blue-green algae since they do not contain phycobilin pigments, do not have lamellae associated with the pigments, produce endospores and are generally much smaller. A brief synopsis of their classification follows, noting only the forms mentioned in the text.

Schizophyta (Bacteria)
    Pseudomonadales (*Hydrogenomonas, Spirillum, Vibrio*)
    Chlamydobacteriales (*Leptothrix, Crenothrix*)
    Eubacteriales (*Corynebacterium, Sarcina, Diplococcus, Staphylococcus, Bacillus*)

Actinomycetales (*Streptomyces*)
Beggiatoales (*Achromatium*)

Cyanophyta (Blue-green algae)
Chroococcales (*Chroococcus, Merismopedia, Microcystis*)
Chamaesiphonales (*Chamaesiphon*)
Hormogonales (*Anabaena, Nostoc, Oscillatoria, Scytonema, Tolypthrix*)

Practical Study

1. Although most bacteria are very small, they can usually be seen using the high power on a student microscope. If available an oil immersion objective should be used. Observe any vegetable or animal matter decaying in water and draw the types of bacteria present. Addition of organic compounds such as sugars, yeast extract, etc., often enhances growth.

2. Prepare Petri dishes containing 2 per cent agar. Expose some to the air and to others add small amounts of fresh or decaying plant or animal remains. Note the form, coloration, etc., of the bacterial colonies which develop. Remove some material from the colonies and illustrate the morphology of the cells. N.B. Yeasts, other fungi and even algae may also grow on the plates and must be distinguished. If agar is not available, gelatin or even table jelly will yield results. Always keep some plates unseeded—you may be surprised how easy it is for contaminants to grow.

3. When studying other biological material keep a constant watch for bacteria in the dying cells. Freshwater and marine algae often have damaged cells within which bacteria grow.

4. Investigate the bacteria in the root nodules of any leguminous plants which may be available.

5. Scrape any bluish-black growths from plant pots, soil, garden paths, etc., mount a little in water on a microscope slide and look for blue-green algae.

6. Shake some of this material (or a little surface soil) in water and spread as a film on an agar surface in a Petri dish. Place some in light and some in the dark and observe the growth of the blue-green algae (and other lower plants!).

7. Look for blue-green algae in freshwater ponds, lakes or on rocks, seaweeds, etc., along the shore. Filamentous species often grow on shallow sediments at the edge of ponds and in small wet depressions in soil, or where water drips out of pipes.

8. Illustrate the form of heterocysts and akinetes in any material

7

you find. Note particularly any forms appearing black under the microscope as they almost certainly contain gas vacuoles.

9. Investigate the difference in morphology between any non-motile and motile forms you encounter.

10. Measure the rate of movement of some species of Cyanophyta. Record any spiral movement, reversals and reactions to light and dark.

Review Questions

1. Describe the group characteristics of Bacteria and Cyanophyta.

2. How do these two groups differ (a) in morphology, (b) in metabolism, (c) in ecology?

3. What part do they play in their natural environment? How important are they?

4. What characters are used to classify these organisms?

5. Why are such apparently simple organisms so successful and abundant?

6. Review their economic importance. How may they be important in (a) water purification, (b) sewage disposal, (c) spoilage of foods and industrial products?

7. Could life exist in a bacteria-free environment?

8. Is there a possible connexion between the simple organization of the nucleus in these groups and the lack of well defined sexual stages?

9. In what ways are these organisms adapted to their environment?

10. How do these two groups differ from the other lower plant groups?

BIBLIOGRAPHY

FRITSCH, F. E., *The Structure and Reproduction of the Algae*, Vol. II, Cambridge University Press, 1945

SALLE, A. J., *Fundamental Principles of Bacteriology*, McGraw-Hill, New York, 1961

2

THE ALGAE—INTRODUCTION AND GREEN PIGMENTED GROUPS

THE algae comprise all the photosynthetic lower plants which have no vascular differentiation into complex anatomical tracts nor a sterile layer of cells forming the gametangial wall.

Algae are morphologically the simplest organisms which possess a nucleus with a bounding membrane, recognizable chromosomes and also assimilate via the photosynthetic system which is basic to all plants containing *chlorophyll a*. The chlorophylls and other pigments are located in plastids, chloroplasts or chromatophores; the latter term being used for plastids in which brown or red pigments mask the green colour of the chlorophyll, e.g. *Fucus*. Otherwise the external morphology ranges from the very simple, e.g. the spherical cell of *Chlorella* (*Figure 2.1*) through colonial (*Volvox*), filamentous (unbranched—*Ulothrix, Spirogyra,* branched—*Cladophora, Ectocarpus*) to thalloid—*Fucus* (*Figures 2.1–3.5*). However large and complex the external morphology may become, and some are much larger and more complex than *Fucus*, there is never any great differentiation of cellular morphology above that comparable to the parenchyma or prosenchyma of higher plants and rarely is there any *pronounced* differentiation into conducting or other specialized tissues. On the other hand internal morphology of the cells is frequently more complex than that of many cell types within higher plants, e.g. a *Chlamydomonas* cell not only has all the nutritional mechanisms of a normal plant but also has an active excretory system, a locomotory system, a sensory system (e.g. it can detect light gradients and move along them) and is capable of reproduction both asexually and sexually. All or most of these attributes are present in the other so-called simple, motile algae, e.g. *Euglena* and *Pinnularia* (a diatom, see p. 35). By the aggregation of cells after division, colonial genera are formed, e.g. the motile *Gonium, Pandorina, Eudorina, Volvox* (*Figure 2.4*), and the non-motile colonies of *Scenedesmus* and *Pediastrum* (*Figure 2.5*). In these all the cells may be equally capable of nutrition, movement and reproduction but in *Eudorina* and *Volvox* specialization has resulted in the restriction of the reproductive process to certain cells. This is even more pronounced in the larger

9

thalloid algae in which parts of the thallus are elaborated into reproductive regions and the cells themselves become modified to form oogonia and antheridia. These are not as complex as those of the Bryophyta in that they are still basically unicellular and without a sterile outer wall such as is common to all Bryophyta and Pteridophyta. An intermediate stage is, however, found in a group of green algae, the stoneworts (Charophyta).

The reproductive processes in algae are themselves perhaps the most varied of any group in the plant kingdom from simple fusion of equal gametes—isogamy—through fusion of unequal gametes—anisogamy—to oogamy in *Volvox, Vaucheria, Fucus* and all the red algae (Rhodophyta). In some diatoms and the conjugate green algae a process of conjugation of non-motile gametes occurs. Asexual reproduction is brought about by the formation of motile zoospores (e.g. *Chlamydomonas*) or non-motile aplanospores (e.g. *Chlorella*) or by vegetative propagation via thick walled resting spores (akinetes), propagules or fragmentation.

All have their photosynthetic pigments located in discrete plastids and in this way differ from the photosynthetic bacteria and the Cyanophyta. Unlike all the remaining lower plants, the algae possess an extraordinary range of pigments and the mixture of these pigments in the plastids gives rise to a variety of colours although photosynthesis is always mediated through *chlorophyll a*. This range of pigmentation is also linked with a variety of metabolic products some of which are unique to the algae.

Ecologically they are the most widespread of the photosynthetic plants, forming the bulk of the carbon assimilating, floating, microscopic cells in the sea and in fresh waters (phytoplankton) and thus forming the primary producers over 70 per cent of the earth's surface. Apart from this floating population all other underwater surfaces, natural or artificial (e.g. the sides of boats below the waterline) are colonized by algae so long as they are within the zone to which photosynthetically usable light penetrates; thus aquatic plants, rocks, sand and mud and even animals, e.g. molluscs and whales may have a coating of motile or attached algae. These may be microscopic but in one well-known habitat—the rocky seashore—apart from the multitude of microscopic species on the rock surface, the inter-tidal and sub-tidal zone is richly colonized by red and brown algae collectively known as seaweeds and these themselves are usually the host to innumerable microscopic forms attached to their surface. On the land, especially in humid tropical regions but also in all other zones, the soil surface supports a very large population of algae frequently visible to the naked eye as a green film. In

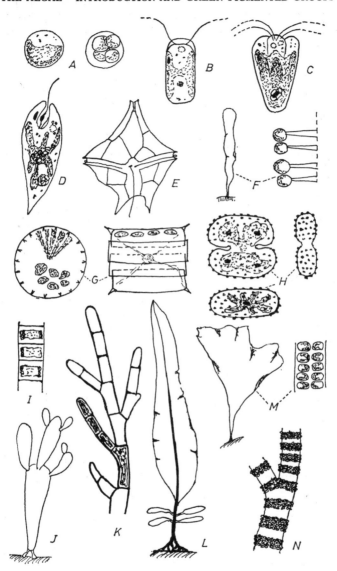

Figure 2.1. The range of algal morphology. A, vegetative cell of Chlorella and formation of autospores; B, Chlamydomonas; C, Pyramimonas; D, Euglena; E, Peridinium; F, thallus of Tetraspora and four cells with pseudocilia; G, valve (left) and girdle (right) views of a centric diatom—Stephanodiscus; H, three views of a desmid—Cosmarium; I, Ulothrix; J, a siphonaceous alga—Valonia; K, Cladophora; L, Alaria; M, thallus and section of Ulva; N, part of the thallus of Ceramium

11

humid regions these algae extend on to the surface of trees and other vegetation and may coat the bark and leaves whilst a few species are actually parasitic on Angiosperms. Finally a small number of algae live on the surface of permanent snow and ice (Kryoflora) amongst which is a *Chlamydomonas* species.

The major importance of algae is that they fix carbon dioxide in habitats where few or no other photosynthetic plants occur. Thus in fresh waters and particularly in the open ocean they are essential to the food chain leading to fish. They are also important sources of chemicals such as agar (used to cultivate bacteria, fungi, algae, etc.), alginic acid (used in the food industry) and as food, especially in the Far East.

The classification of algae is complex owing to the great diversity of morphology, pigmentation and reproductive processes, but subdivision into fairly discrete groups (divisions and classes) is essential to avoid the apparent chaos when the whole range is contemplated. The use of the electron microscope has added greatly to our knowledge of the structure of algae and has also resulted in the redefining of certain groups; much still remains to be studied. The early systems of classification were based on pigmentation which is in fact a biochemical criterion and this is still of value in delimiting large groups such as the green (Chlorophyta), brown (Phaeophyta) and red algae (Rhodophyta). Coupling coloration with morphology enables other large groups to be distinguished, for example brown pigmented unicells with a discrete silica wall (recognizable by the characteristic markings on it) form the large group known as the diatoms (Bacillariophyta). Yet again brown unicells with characteristic lateral and transverse furrows and often with a cell wall composed of numerous plates comprise the phylum Dinophyta. Brown pigmented, free living cells with various arrangements of the flagella form the two groups Chrysophyta and Haptophyceae, although some non-motile and even filamentous forms also occur in these groups and are difficult to distinguish from Phaeophyta until the reproductive cells are seen. A group of green algae (Xanthophyta) not included within the Chlorophyta are difficult to characterize briefly but are not likely to be found in abundance— they differ from the Chlorophyta in that the chromatophores are always discoid (and such occur only in one complex marine group of Chlorophyta) and the cells are often, though indistinctly, formed of two halves. Two other separate green groups are the Euglenophyta and Charophyta, the former being unicells with apparently a single flagellum (a second is present but does not extend from the apical invagination), whilst the latter are

12

macrophytic, branching plants with branches arising in whorls at the nodes. Yet another green pigmented group has motile cells with four thick flagella arising from an apical pit (Prasinophyceae). These types are characterized in *Figure 2.1*.

The classical concept of the 'green algae' has been modified considerably in recent years and it is now obvious that several distinct assemblages of algae all possess *chlorophyll a* and *b* as a basic denominator and some have been elevated to the status of phyla (division) whilst others remain as classes until further detailed studies have been completed. The use of genetic and biochemical characters and above all the greater precision and detail observable using electron microscope techniques is making the consideration of the taxonomy of this group a fascinating study.

Euglenophyta

Many genera of this group are colourless organisms and are best considered as Protozoa but the well-known genus *Euglena* is pigmented and is at least partially autotrophic. One species has been grown in a completely defined chemical medium though all seem to require organic growth factors such as vitamins—this is, however, not unusual in other algal groups. *Euglena* and related genera are exceedingly common in polluted water owing to this requirement for organic factors; they are readily obtainable by sampling either the water or more surely the sediments of farm ponds. They also occur on soils, in all fresh waters and in brackish habitats but more rarely in marine habitats. It is only in the last decade that the cell structure of *Euglena* has been adequately investigated and hence almost all textbook accounts are unavoidably misleading. Much of the detail can only be ascertained from thin sections examined under the electron microscope. The genus is unicellular, radial or somewhat flattened and of very diverse shape (see *Figure 2.2 A–C* for some examples). Likewise the green chromatophores are variously shaped and possess pyrenoids. *Euglena* has the surprising feature that it can be 'cured' of its chromatophores by heat or streptomycin treatment and the resulting colourless cells behave as protozoa. A characteristic of *Euglena* is the spirally striate pellicle which is pliable and allows the cell to assume a variety of shapes—metaboly—an unfortunate term. This has recently been shown to be due to the structural arrangement of a series of pellicular strips which are wound round the cell like a bandage and which can slide over one another (*Figure 2.2 I*). Outside this is the cell membrane so that in reality the pellicular strips form an endoskeleton. At the cell apex and base the strips fuse and at the apex pass down into an anterior invagination which is not a gullet since it is not in any way associated with ingestion of solid particles. At the base of this invagination arise the two flagella, one short and never protruding beyond the mouth of the invagination and the other long and extending out to the exterior as the locomotory flagellum. It has a single row of fine hairs along its length and also a swelling, the 'photoreceptor', near its entry into the cell. The shorter flagellum is devoid of hairs. Free in the cytoplasm, usually at the apical end, is a large red stigma and a main contractile vacuole with a ring of collecting vacuoles around it. The nucleus is often obscured by the numerous chromatophores and the large glistening bodies which are a storage product akin to starch and known as paramylum. These paramylum granules are often a very characteristic shape and give an unmistakable clue to the euglenoid nature of such flagellates when encountered in a sample.

The closely related genera are also readily recognizable— *Trachelomonas* is a euglenoid cell with all the above features but encased in a firm theca which has a pore through which the flagellum protrudes (*Figure 2.2 F–H*). The thecae are often strikingly coloured brown or black by the deposition of iron and manganese compounds in the thecal material so that the cell within is not easy to observe. Young daughter cells have very thin thecae and may be confused at first with *Euglena*. Flattened and often twisted euglenoid cells are referred to the genus *Phacus*. The disc-like forms (*Figure 2.2 D*) are easily recognized but some of the small elongate species are difficult to distinguish from certain *Euglena* species. There is a tendency to regard *Euglena* as the prime euglenoid since it is usually chosen as the type for study, but both *Trachelomonas* and *Phacus* are as widespread and common.

Reproduction of euglenoids is by longitudinal fission starting at the apex and proceeding downwards. The nuclear division is rather unusual in that the nuclear membrane does not break down but merely constricts to separate the daughter groups of chromosomes and eventually is merely a thread between the two groups which then breaks—a similar type of nuclear division occurs in dinoflagellates. A very recent discovery is the finding of endogenous bacteria within the nucleus of some euglenoid species—in *Trachelomonas* they also occur in the cytoplasm. Resting stages are sometimes found in which the cells round up and become surrounded by mucilage. Sexual reproduction is apparently rare but has been recorded in some *Euglena* species.

This group is fascinating because many species have been used

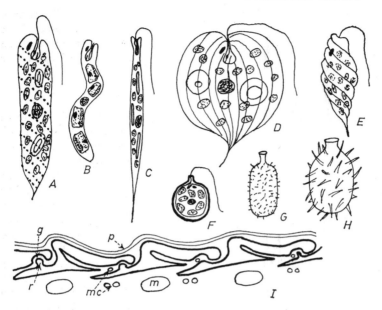

Figure 2.2. Euglenophyta. A, B, C, three examples of Euglena; *D, E, a flattened and a spirally twisted* Phacus; *F, G, H, three species of* Trachelomonas; *I, a cross-section of the pellicular strips of* Euglena *as seen in the electron microscope. The ridge (r) of each pellicular strip fits into the groove (g) of the adjacent. The plasmalemma (p) is on the outside. Muciferous bodies (m) occur beneath each pellicular strip and microtubules (mc) occur beneath and between the strips. (Modified from* Leedale[3]*)*

as tools to investigate biochemical, physiological and ecological phenomena—indeed a whole book has been devoted to these aspects of *Euglena* (see References, p. 34).

E. gracilis has a nutritional requirement for the vitamin B complex and hence cultures of this euglenoid can be grown in a basic nutrient medium to which liquids containing the vitamin can be added, and by measuring the growth of the *Euglena* either by cell counts or by extracting its chlorophyll and by comparison with growths obtained in media containing known amounts of vitamin, the amount in the sample can be estimated. Euglenoids are positively phototactic and this ability to move towards light has been utilized in investigating aspects of the mechanism of phototaxis, e.g. the effect of different wavelengths of light. A rhythmic response to light has also been found in that the *Euglena* swims towards the light during light periods with peak activity round midday, but does not respond during the night. In natural habitats on estuarial muds some *Euglena* species emerge from below the mud surface during daytime

15

exposure by the outgoing tide and reburrow *before* the tide returns. Cells transferred to constant conditions in the laboratory continue this rhythm for many days without any entraining stimulus such as is supplied in nature by alternating light/dark and periodic cover by the tides.

Prasinophyceae

This is a relatively new grouping of algae which previously were placed in the Chlorophyta. Some are flagellate with four thick flagella emerging from an apical pit, e.g. *Pyramimonas* (*Figure 2.1 C*) whilst others are coccoid or colonial. The common green sphere (*Halosphaera*) occurring in oceanic plankton belongs here and under certain conditions produces motile cells similar to the free living species. This group is intriguing since it is only with the aid of the electron microscope that the characters can be recognized and the affinities of the several genera determined. Admittedly even the light-microscopists recognized that these genera were in some ways subtly different from other green genera and doubt arose as to their taxonomic position. One of the most unexpected aspects of this work has been the revelation that scales of various kinds can be produced within the cells and then deposited onto the surface not only of the cells but along the flagella as well.

Chlorophyta

Unlike the two previous groups this phylum contains a large number of seemingly diverse algae. However, they have many common features—thus the motile cells, zoospores or motile gametes have two smooth flagella (occasionally two pairs), the cell walls contain cellulose and pectin, starch is the common reserve product and the vegetative cells are haploid and uninucleate. These are generalizations and there are obviously a few exceptional genera, some of which may on further investigation warrant moving into other groups such as has already been done for the genera of the Prasinophyceae. These movements of genera may seem confusing but in fact they lead to better circumscribed groups without the anomalous genera which has been a characteristic of certain systematic works in the past.

Five distinct lines of morphological development are found in this phylum—flagellate, tetrasporal, coccoid, filamentous and thalloid (*Figures 2.3–2.7*). In the first two the cells may be free living, e.g. *Chlamydomonas* and *Chlorella*, or they may aggregate to form colonies, e.g. *Volvox* and *Pediastrum*. Tetrasporal genera are those in which the

16

vegetative cells are immersed in a mass of mucilage, e.g. *Tetraspora*. The filamentous forms may be uniseriate, e.g. *Ulothrix*, or branching, e.g. *Stigeoclonium*. The thalloid forms consist of parenchymatous sheets of cells either double, e.g. the common sea lettuce, *Ulva*, or tubular, e.g. the equally common *Enteromorpha*.

Chlorophyceae

This class contains all the flagellate, coccoid and filamentous groups reproducing by means of biflagellate swarmers (or gametes) and in which the cells in general are uninucleate.

Chlamydomonas is very common in fresh waters and on soils but is often difficult to find since the cells are usually small and fast swimming—it is often easier to detect if a small amount of water from just above the sediment or from amongst attached algae is spread over a layer of 2 per cent agar in a Petri dish—the individual cells tend to multiply forming palmelloid stages, these can then be transferred to liquid cultures or the plate can be flooded with sterilized pond water to get the vegetative motile stage. *Chlamydomonas* is at first sight a simple genus of unicellular biflagellate alga containing a single chromatophore and surrounded by a cellulose cell wall. For many decades it has been a standard type studied by generations of students—unfortunately it is often so small that little detail can be made out. However, study one example isolated from its natural habitat and bear in mind the extent of variation inherent in this genus of many hundred species. Some characteristics of the individual motile cells used to delimit species are, size, shape, form of chromatophore, occurrence and position of pyrenoid and related starch, position of the eyespot, and length of flagella.

The cell itself is surrounded by a rigid cell wall which is probably composed of cellulose microfibrils and provided with two pores through which the flagella emerge. The cytoplasmic membrane may be closely adpressed to this wall or may be attached over only a small area. Outside the cell wall there is often a layer of mucilage which may be thick and visible or extremely thin or absent. Most *Chlamydomonas* species investigated have been shown to secrete polysaccharide material into the external medium and the forms with noticeable mucilage may be those in which this extracellular material remains for a time as a capsule around the cell. Occasionally striations are visible on the cell wall and sometimes it is coloured by salts taken up from the medium in which the cells are growing. The cytoplasmic membrane extends through the pores in the cell wall to form the tubular membranes of the flagella. Within these tubes occur the nine peripheral double fibrils and two central single

17

fibrils characteristic of flagella (see p. 38 for an exception to this rule). This membrane is smooth, i.e. without the fine hairs with which some other flagella membranes are furnished, e.g. *Euglena*. The flagella vary in length but are frequently about the same length

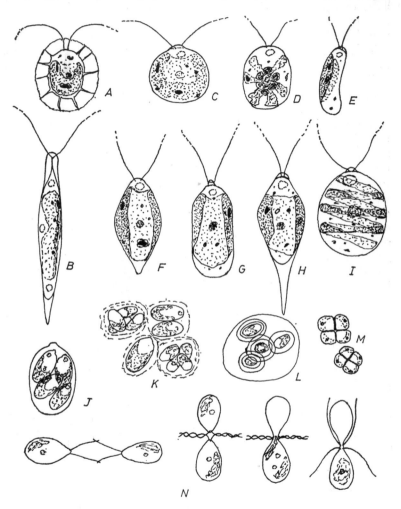

Figure 2.3. Unicells of the Volvocales. A, Haematococcus; *B,* Chlorogonium; *C–I, various morphological forms of* Chlamydomonas, *showing range of shape and chloroplast form; J, formation of zoospores in* Chlamydomonas; *K,* 'Palmella' *stage of* Chlamydomonas; *L,* 'Gloeocystis' *stage of* Chlamydomonas; *M,* 'Tetracoccus' *stage of* Chlamydomonas; *N, diagrammatic representation of fusion of* Chlamydomonas *gametes and formation of zygote (C–I after Ettl)*

as the cell; they are very fine and are often difficult to see. In some species the tips of the flagella narrow to fine 'whiplash' points. Movement of the flagella is of a 'breast stroke' nature with about 10–12 beats per second at 20°C. The forward movement is associated with the backward stroke of the flagella and is accompanied by a rotation of the cells.

The external morphology varies from spherical, ovoid, pear-shaped, semi-circular to cylindrical (*Figure 2.3 C–I*).

Within the outer cytoplasmic membrane occur all the normal organelles—chloroplast, nucleus, dictyosome(s) (Golgi body), endoplasmic reticulum, granules, and vacuoles. The illustrations show something of the range of chloroplast shape, cup-shaped, H-shaped, stellate, plate-like and reticulate. There is in some species a reduction in chloroplast size so that it only occupies part of the cell, whilst in others numerous discoid chloroplasts occur. A genus *Polytoma* is known in which the cell is identical with *Chlamydomonas* except that the chloroplast is absent and it is often assumed that *Polytoma* has arisen from *Chlamydomonas* by loss of the chloroplasts although it is not possible to confirm this. However, many viable mutant forms have been induced in *Chlamydomonas*, some of which are lacking certain of the chloroplast pigments. One, two or more pyrenoids may be present, embedded within the chloroplast and surrounded by starch grains; the latter may also be distributed within the chloroplast without any apparent relation to a pyrenoid. One other structure is contained within the chloroplast and that is the eyespot; it consists of a row of carotenoid granules located between lamellae, usually but not always at the anterior end of the cell. The other organelles of the cytoplasm are difficult to observe in living material although under favourable conditions two contractile vacuoles, usually near the base of the flagella, and a nucleus in the centre of the cell can be seen. Other structures seen under the electron microscope are the Golgi bodies (dictyosomes) and mitochondria—the latter are scattered around the nucleus and chloroplast.

In *Chlamydomonas* there is no vegetative division in the motile stage by longitudinal cleavage of the protoplast as in flagellates such as *Euglena*. Growth of the cell is confined to expansion accompanied by the formation of metabolic products some of which are stored in the cell whilst others diffuse out of the cell into the medium (misleadingly termed extracellular products). Ultimately the cells form spores or gametes. The simplest type of formation is the rounding up of the cytoplasm which then becomes surrounded by a thick wall to form an aplanospore within the original cell membrane. Asexual reproduction occurs by the longitudinal cleavage of the

19

cytoplasm within the mother cell wall. There is often rotation of the cytoplasm so that the 2, 4 or 8 daughter cells (zoospores) lie trans-verse to the original axis. Prior to asexual division of the cell the parent flagella are either thrown off or withdraw into the cytoplasm. The daughter cells each form a new cell wall and new flagella, usually prior to release from the parent membrane. Some species under certain environmental conditions form spores devoid of flagella; the parent membrane becomes mucilaginous and the spores remain within the mucilage and continue to divide (*Figure 2.3 K*). This type of division results in a 'palmella' stage, which in some ways resembles the alga *Palmella*. Occasionally the cells in this mucilaginous phase are each surrounded by a number of concentric spheres of mucilage to form a 'gloeocystis' stage (*Figure 2.3 L*), which resembles the alga *Gloeocystis*. In either of these types the cells may secrete thick walls; the cells are then often termed akinetes or hypnospores. In at least one species the non-motile cells divide without the formation of mucilage to give tetrads of cells which has been termed a '*Tetracoccus*' stage (*Figure 2.3 M*).

Sexual reproduction is affected by the fusion of gametes produced in a manner similar to that of the zoospores. Most species are iso-gamous, that is the gametes are equal in size. They tend to be smaller than zoospores and are produced in larger numbers, 16, 32 or 64 in each cell, resembling small *Chlamydomonas* cells. There is no cell wall surrounding the gamete but in some the outer cytoplasmic membrane is relatively rigid and is left behind when fusion occurs. Anisogamy occurs in *C. braunii* where the larger gametes are formed in fours within the parent cells whilst the microgametes are twice as numerous. In *C. coccifera* some vegetative cells become converted without cell division into a single large gamete whilst other cells give rise to sixteen smaller gametes; this situation may be termed oogamy, the large gamete acting as an ovum and the smaller ones as spermatozooids. In *C. moewusii* (=*C. eugametos*) the gametes appear to be ordinary cells released from the parent cell wall. This species is heterothallic, i.e. the parent cells are of two different physiological types usually designated 'plus' and 'minus' and only when these two types are mixed will sexual fusion result. Prior to fusion 'clumping' occurs, whereby groups of gametes aggregate together; this is said to be due to a 'stickiness' of the flagella of the 'plus' and 'minus' mating types. The clumps may consist of a few or up to 100 gametes and this clumping occurs within a few minutes of the mixing of the opposite gamete types.

The gametes appear to pair within the clumps by the attraction of the flagella tips, which first adhere together and then the rest of the flagella come to lie together, thus bringing the apical papillae adjacent to one another. Across these papillae a cytoplasmic bridge is established and soon after this the flagella disengage again commencing the process at the distal ends (*Figure 2.3 N*). At this stage the copulants lose any tendency to stay within the clump and they swim away. Instead of both pairs of flagella beating and possibly causing random movement, only one pair of flagella beat whilst those of the cell which is in an anterior position lie alongside the driving posterior cell (*Figure 2.3 N*).

Clumping can be produced by the addition of cell-free filtrate from a culture of one mating type to a culture of gametes of the opposite type (auto-agglutination); it does not, however, result in pairing or zygote formation.

The life cycle and nuclear cycle of *C. reinhardi* has been studied in detail since this organism can be readily grown on agar plates or in liquid culture and has yielded numerous biochemical mutants after treatment with ultra-violet light or X-rays. If cells grown on agar plates are suspended in a culture medium they differentiate into gametes after 2–4 hours in the light; this is related to depletion of nitrogen in the cells. At this stage, mixing of gametes of opposite mating types results in 'clumping', followed by pairing, and 10–15 minutes later, quadriflagellate binucleate cells (zygotes) are formed. If these are then placed on agar plates, fusion of the nuclei occurs some 12–14 hours later. The zygotes, after loss of the flagella, enlarge to about twice the original diameter and then require a period of time for maturation, approximately six days at 25°C, the first 18 hours in the light and the remaining time in the dark. After this time re-plating on fresh agar in the light results in germination, which takes 15–24 hours, during which the zygote wall ruptures and four (sometimes eight) *non-motile* haploid cells are extruded. These are produced by meiotic division and half are the 'plus' mating type and half the 'minus'. Meiosis in a population of zygotes is apparently synchronous. The haploid number of chromosomes in *C. reinhardi* is 8. Many mutants of this alga have been artificially induced, e.g. eyespotless, flagella-less, pigment deficient, non-heterotrophic, non-autotrophic, arginine dependent, acetate requiring, etc., and many of the genes responsible for these characters have been mapped on the eight chromosomes in relation to the centromeres.

The genus is extremely wide in its distribution, occurring in fresh, brackish and marine habitats. They are found under extreme conditions on the surface of permanent ice and snowfields, where they often colour the surface red due to the accumulation of carotenoid pigments in the cells and particularly in the zygotes. They occur as epiphytes on tree bark and in the slime on the fruit bodies of fungi. One of their characteristic habitats is on the surface of soil. In permanent waters (ponds, lakes, etc.) they are present as free swimming components of the phytoplankton and occur in all types of waters from extremely nutrient poor moorland waters, to rich farmyard ponds. Even in inorganic polluted waters such as acid, mine waste waters a small number of characteristic *Chlamydomonas* species live. The surface sediment in ponds and lakes is a very rich source of species and many of them may be confined to this habitat. Of a more specialized character are the forms which live epibiotic-ally, for example in empty thecae of the alga *Dinobryon*, in the mucilage of other algae, in frog spawn, attached to some animals (e.g. Rotifers) and in the mucilage surrounding many water plants. In brackish waters they occur on the surface soil and in the ponds on salt marshes, and in marine habitats in rock pools, particularly in the region around high tide level. *Chlamydomonas* is purposely dealt with in detail to show how complex an apparently simple lower plant can be—similar details characterize many others (e.g. yeasts, p. 76).

Other unicellular types related to *Chlamydomonas* are *Carteria* with 4 flagella, *Haematococcus* with a thick wall into which fibrils of the cells appear to pass (*Figure 2.3 A*) and *Chlorogonium* which is extremely elongate (*Figure 2.3 B*). Several colonial genera are simpler in organization than the commonly studied *Volvox*, e.g. in *Gonium* the *Chlamydomonas*-like cells are arranged as a flat, slightly curved plate (*Figure 2.4*) and in *Pandorina* as a globose bunch of cells without much free space between them. *Volvox* is the largest of the colonial genera and even moderately sized colonies are visible to the naked eye as yellowish globules spinning around in the water. These colonial genera are planktonic—that is free-living in a body of water. The yellowish colour of *Volvox* is produced by the dispersion of the green cells in a superficial layer of the colony or coenobium with copius mucilage filling the remainder of the sphere. Of all these coenobial forms, *Volvox* is least like *Chlamydomonas* since it has filamentous connexions which pass through the individual mucilage layers around each cell and join with those adjacent cells (*Figure 2.4*). Asexual reproduction involves extensive longitudinal division of one or more vegetative cells which owing to the pressure of space bulge inwards forming a flask of cells. The basic polarity of the cells is unaltered during these divisions so that the flagella ends are all pointing towards the centre of the flask—evection then occurs and the whole structure turns itself inside out to form the young daughter colony which often remains within the parent colony and even swims

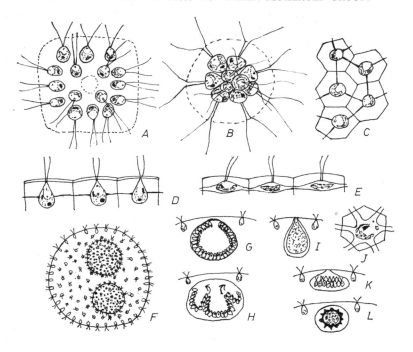

Figure 2.4. Colonial forms of the Volvocales. A, Gonium; *B,* Pandorina; *C, cells of* Volvox aureus *in surface view; D, cells of* Volvox aureus *in transverse section; E, cells of* Volvox globator *in transverse section; F,* Volvox *colony with young daughter colonies inside; G, H, formation of young daughter colonies and evection to place the flagellar poles of the cells onto the outside; I, formation of egg cell in* Volvox; *J, surface view of a cell of* Volvox globator; *K, formation of a 'plate' of male gametes; L, zygote surrounded by an ornamented wall*

around inside (*Figure 2.4 F*). Sexual reproduction again involves certain of the vegetative cells—the genus is oogamous, hence some cells enlarge and lose their flagella to form eggs. Other superficial cells undergo longitudinal division to form a round plate of cells all with flagella which are released as an aggregate and then separate and swim off to function as male gametes. The zygote slowly forms a thick ornamented wall around itself and frequently falls towards the centre of the coenobium where it remains until the colony decays. On germination the contents are released as a single swarmer which then cleaves to form a number of vegetative cells which organize themselves into a new colony. *Volvox* is of spasmodic occurrence in nature so that unlike *Chlamydomonas* it is not always readily available for study.

23

Tetrasporal organization is probably the least common life form amongst green algae. *Tetraspora (Figure 2.1 F)* itself forms a mucilaginous mass often several centimetres in length attached to stones or water plants. The cells are often grouped in fours in the surface mucilage and paired channels pass through the mucilage giving the impression of flagella. Recent electron microscope studies have shown that although flagella bases occur in the cells only a few microfibrils extend into the channels through the mucilage.

The most well known and famous or infamous of all algae is a representative of the coccoid organization—*Chlorella (Figure 2.1A).* Famous because so much basic plant physiology and biochemistry has been carried out using this genus, which grows rapidly, is merely a non-motile spherical cell, reproducing simply by dividing into four small cells which then expand to the parent size before dividing again. Infamous because being a spherical unicell it is difficult to categorize the species and varieties, is almost uninvestigated in its natural habitats and so tolerant of a wide range of cultural conditions that for example it will grow in distilled water bottles, weak acid and alkali bottles, etc., so that results obtained from its study may have little relevance to the behaviour of other algae. As for *Euglena,* a whole book could be devoted to this simple spherical alga with its fairly resistant wall and cup-shaped chromatophore. It is one of the few algae which have been grown in synchronous culture so that all the cells in the culture are in phase with one another and all divide at the same time. This means that large numbers of cells can be harvested at any chosen stage in the cycle from division through maturation to the next division and the physiology and biochemistry of each stage studied—in normal cultures there is a mixture of cells of all ages and in all stages of division and even senescence and resting. Many experiments have been performed to test the feasibility of growing algae for food and in these *Chlorella* has featured prominently.

An alga very similar to *Chlorella* is *Chlorococcum*, which only differs from the former in that on division instead of forming four cells which are in fact miniatures of the parent cell (autospores) the *Chlorococcum* cell cleaves to form biflagellate zoospores which soon lose their flagella and expand to form the typical vegetative cell. Almost all of the Chlorococcales reproduce by one or the other of these methods. Many genera are colonial and the form of the colony is very definitive for each genus and some representative forms are illustrated in *Figure 2.5.*

Ulothrix is the only common example of the unbranched filamentous habit and this is readily obtained from soil samples plated

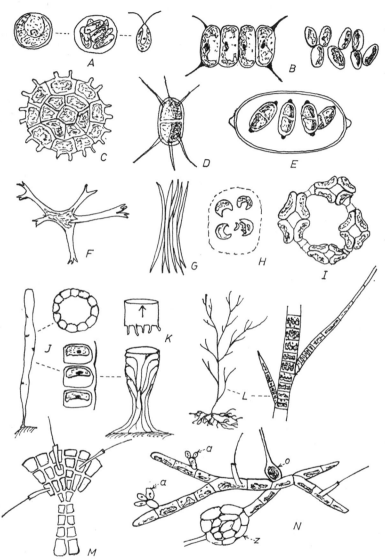

Figure 2.5. Coccoid and filamentous Chlorophyta. A, cell of Chlorococcum *and formation of planospores; B, two colonies of* Scenedesmus; *C,* Pediastrum; *D,* Chodatella; *E,* Oocystis—*cell with autospores; F,* Tetraedron; *G,* Ankistrodesmus; *H,* Kirchneriella, *one cell producing autospores; I,* Crucigenia; *J,* Enteromorpha *plant and on right transverse and longitudinal section; K, upper, cut segment with rhizoids developing at base, and below, the holdfast system of* Enteromorpha; *L, plant and segment of branching filament of* Stigeoclonium; *M,* Coleochaete scutata; *N,* Coleochaete pulvinata. *Antheridia (a) and oogonia (o), zygote (z) enclosed in filaments. Note sheathed hairs in both* Coleochaete *species*

25

out on agar. The cells have simple band-shaped chromatophores.

The macroscopic parenchymatous thalli of *Ulva* and *Entero-morpha* are abundant on almost all rocky shores where they form extensive growths attached to rocks and seaweeds. *Enteromorpha* is particularly frequent at the top of the shore particularly where fresh water filters on to the shore. *Ulva (Figure 2.1 M)* is more scattered in the inter-tidal and sub-tidal zones. The thallus of the latter is formed of a double layer of cells each containing a cup-shaped chromatophore. Towards the base the cells grow downwards as hyphae and form the attachment organ. The life history is straightforward—the gametophytes produce biflagellate gametes and fusion is only between two gametes from different thalli (heterothallism). Zygotes germinate immediately to form the sporophyte which is morphologically identical to the gametophyte (isomorphic) but is diploid and this produces quadriflagellate zoospores which then germinate to reconstitute the sexual plants. The related *Enteromorpha (Figure 2.5 J)* is tubular and many species are markedly polarized with the cup-shaped chromatophores in the upper halves of the cells. Attachment is similar to that in *Ulva*. An interesting property of *Enteromorpha* thalli is their ability to heal wounds and in some cases to form rhizoids from the wound surface. In the polarized forms this rhizoid formation is also polarized so that it only occurs at the lowermost cut surface and not at the upper if a segment is cut transversely out of the thallus. The lengths of rhizoids so formed increase down the thallus and many interesting experiments can be performed with these plants.

The branching filamentous genera are almost all collected into a single order, the Chaetophorales, the majority of which are attached forms growing on stones or on other plants. Many genera form hair-like outgrowths and have a heteromorphic growth of the thalli with the production of basal attaching filaments and upright photosynthetic filaments (heterotrichy). One of the simplest of these is *Stigeoclonium (Figure 2.5 L)* and this illustrates all the above points, basal filaments, and upright filaments which end in hair points composed of thin cells. The cells have band-shaped chloroplasts. The degree to which the basal and upright system is developed varies between the genera and even between species in a genus. Perhaps one of the most advanced forms in the green algae is *Coleochaete* which illustrates this very point—*C. scutata* has the basal filaments fused to form a disc and has no upright filaments whereas *C. pulvinata* has basal and upright filaments all enclosed in a globule of mucilage. Some cells of *Coleochaete* produce long sheathed hairs *(Figure 2.5 M, N)* which are a characteristic of this genus. Sexual

26

reproduction is almost as highly evolved as in the Charophyta (see p. 30). Small branch cells produce single biflagellate male gametes which are devoid of chloroplasts. Other cells of the thallus enlarge and become flask-shaped—the long neck forming a tube down which the male gamete passes. Protection of the zygote is effected by upward growth of filaments around it. The thick-walled zygote segments to form 16–32 cells each of which releases a large zoospore which escapes and germinates to form the mature plant.

Oedogoniophyceae

This small class contains filamentous green algae which are unbranched (*Oedogonium, Figure 2.6 B*) or branched with bulbous based hairs (*Bulbochaete*). They are both quite common, growing only in fresh water, usually on macrophytes—indeed *Oedogonium* is perhaps one of the commonest filamentous algae. They have a very characteristic mode of cell division which results in small pieces of cell wall being left as *caps* at the apices of some of the cells. Oogamy is the rule in sexual reproduction and the male cells and also the zoospores have a characteristic ring of paired flagella (*Figure 2.6 B*). The male gametes are often formed from *dwarf male* plants (*dm, Figure 2.6 A, B*) which grow attached to the filaments or to the oogonia.

Conjugatophyceae

It is relatively uncommon to find a group in which the genera so clearly belong together on features of cytology, reproduction and ecology yet exhibit two quite different morphological growth forms. The commonest genera in this class are the unicellular desmids *Cosmarium, Closterium* and *Staurastrum* and the unbranched filamentous genera *Zygnema, Mougeotia* and *Spirogyra*. They occur exclusively in fresh waters where the majority of species have a distinct preference for acidic waters.

The desmids are some of the most elegant algae—each cell is composed of two halves (semicells) joined together by a bevelled edge at the isthmus. Each mature semicell is ornamented or produced into spines and looked at from the apices is constructed on a bilateral (e.g. *Cosmarium, Figure 2.1 H*) or triangular basis (e.g. *Staurastrum, Figure 2.6 L*). Some cells are extremely flattened, even plate-like, e.g. *Micrasterias*. The cellulose walls are variously ornamented and with numerous pores through which mucilage is extruded and within which the cell is often embedded. Few other green algae have such complex chloroplasts—there are two common types, axial with plate-like extensions, e.g. *Cosmarium*, and

27

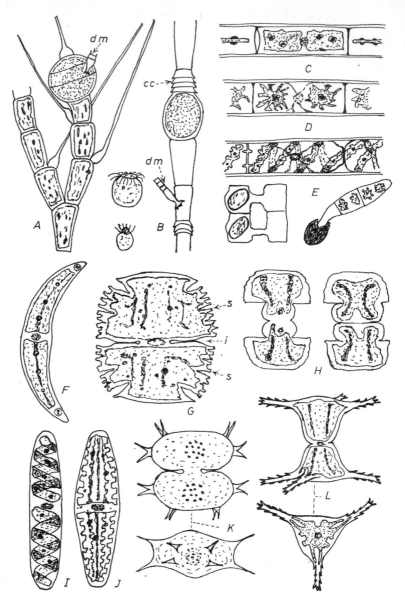

Figure 2.6. Oedogoniophyceae and Conjugatophyceae. A, Bulbochaete *with oogonium and dwarf male plant (dm) attached; B,* Oedogonium *with oogonium in the filament, cap cells (cc) and dwarf male filament (dm). On the left a multiflagellate zoospore and gamete; C,* Mougeotia; *D,* Zygnema; *E,* Spirogyra, *vegetative filament and below left two zygotes in a filament and (right) a germinating zygote of* Zygnema; *F,* Closterium; *G,* Micrasterias (s) semicell and isthmus (t); *H, two stages in the vegetative division of* Cosmarium; *I,* Spirotaenia; *J,* Netrium; *K,* Xanthidium, *above, side view and below viewed from the apex of a semicell; L, similar views of* Staurastrum

parietal spirals, e.g. *Spirotaenia* (*Figure 2.6 I*). The nucleus is situated in the isthmus and a characteristic of the cytology is the large number of chromosomes in some species, e.g. 592 have been recorded in *Netrium*. Desmids divide vegetatively by a pushing apart of the semicells at the isthmus and growth of two new semicells (*Figure 2.6 H*)—thus every desmid cell consists of a parent semicell and a daughter semicell. In some genera the daughter cells do not separate and filaments are formed—these are, however, clearly of desmid structure and cannot be confused with simple filamentous forms. Sexual reproduction involves a process termed conjugation in which two cells come to lie together in a common mucilage envelope—the cells split apart at the isthmus and the nuclei plus some cytoplasm of each cell escape and fuse. The resulting zygote produces a thick, often spiney, wall which bursts on germination and the contents escape. The nucleus undergoes meiotic division and frequently two of the haploid nuclei disintegrate whilst the cytoplasm cleaves around the other two which develop into a pair of desmid cells.

A small sub-group of desmids are cylindrical and without a median constriction, e.g. *Spirotaenia* and *Netrium*. This latter group is often regarded as closely related to the filamentous genera since both have simple unornamented walls. The three genera *Zygnema*, *Mougeotia* and *Spirogyra* (*Figure 2.6 C–E*) are all equally common and all equally difficult to classify into species since taxonomists have found the vegetative characters difficult to use and therefore have resorted to the characters of the zygote wall. However, the three genera are readily distinguished—*Zygnema* has two stellate chromatophores per cell, *Mougeotia* one plate-like plastid and *Spirogyra* one or usually several spirally wound parietal plastids. All have pyrenoids and form starch, as indeed do all Conjugatophyceae. Conjugation is similar to that in the desmids—filaments come to lie side by side in a common mucilage sheath, projections grow out from the adjacent cells pushing the filaments apart—eventually a conjugation tube is formed into which the nuclei and cytoplasm pass and fusion occurs. The zygote surrounds itself with a thick wall and usually drops out of the filament—on germination reduction division takes place and all but one nucleus disintegrates—the germling pushes out and normal cell division commences to form the filament. There are various modifications of the conjugation process, e.g. sometimes the nuclei from one filament move over completely into the adjacent filament and in others the adjacent cells of a single filament conjugate by forming a tube by passing the cross walls. Some species are homothallic whilst others

29

are heterothallic, i.e. require the fusion of nuclei from two different strains.

Bryopsidophyceae

The green algae have exploited a great range of morphological variants and the Bryopsidophyceae illustrate the possibilities of siphonaceous construction. All these algae are coenocytic or semi-coenocytic, that is, without cross walls or with cross walls delimiting multinucleate portions of the thallus. This is one of the fascinating groups where many details of life history still require study; in general the large vegetative thalli are diploid rather than haploid which was the case in the Chlorophyceae. However, heteromorphic alternation of generations is a feature of some genera, e.g. the filamentous *Urospora* which has an alternating unicellular *Codiolum* stage. Two other important features of the group relate to the wall structure, for here occur the very elegant, cellulose, microfibrillar walls of the Cladophorales, whilst in other groups the polymers are based on mannose or xylose rather than glucose and the microfibrils are less well defined. There is also frequent deposition of calcium carbonate around and between the segments of the thalli. The group is very largely marine and many genera form extensive sub-tidal swards in tropical and sub-tropical waters. The extensive calcification of the thalli has resulted in the preservation of many fossil forms.

One of the simplest completely siphonaceous genera is *Bryopsis* (*Figure 2.7 A*) which is a simple, pinnately branched siphon. When several siphons aggregate and also produce lateral branches then very large and varied growths can result, e.g. *Dasycladus* and *Caulerpa*. The common fresh water and marine genus *Cladophora* (*Figure 2.1 K*) consists of multinucleate cells forming a branching thallus—it is common in flowing water and marine rock pools—and is often a rich source of epiphytic diatoms and other algae.

Charophyta

All the genera of this small group of algae are macroscopic, growing rooted by means of rhizoids in the sediment at the bottom of fresh water or brackish ponds. The upright photosynthetic part consists of one or more central axes built up from alternating small nodal cells and very elongate internodal cells (*Figure 2.7 D, E*). The latter never branch but the nodal cells form a ring of branches each of which is built up of similar nodal and internodal cells. Growth is by apical-cells at the apices of each branch cutting

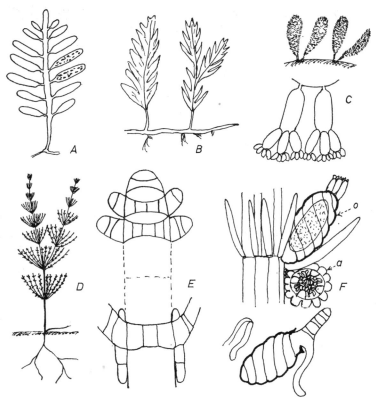

Figure 2.7. Bryopsidophyceae and Charophyta. A, Bryopsis; *B,* Caulerpa; *C, four* Dasycladus *plants and below a section showing branches growing out from the central siphon; D,* Chara; *E, diagram of cell division at the apex of* Chara *and the formation of side branches and corticating filaments; F, above—node of* Chara *with oogonium (o) and antheridium (a), and below, a biflagellate gamete and the germination of the oospore*

off basal cells which differentiate alternately into nodal and internodal cells. In *Chara* the rings of branches at the nodes also give rise to downwardly growing branches which curve around the internodal cell—such a system is called cortication. Many of these plants precipitate crystals of calcium carbonate on the surface. The cells contain numerous discoid chloroplasts which can frequently be seen streaming up and down in the corticating filaments or in the internodal cells. Reproduction is oogamous and the large egg cell formed at a node is protected by curving rows of 'corticating' filaments which grow around it (*Figure 2.7 F*). Also formed at the nodes are the male gametangia and these are exceptional in the algae in that they have a multicellular wall of sterile cells whilst internally a columella bears numerous filaments, each cell of which gives rise to a coiled, elongate, biflagellate male gamete. These gametes are more like those of Bryophytes than algae (*Figure 2.7 F*). The fertilized egg cell surrounds itself with a thick wall and drops off the plant complete with its protective corticating layer. Ultimately it germinates in a 'seed-like' manner producing rhizoids and an upright vegetative shoot which becomes segmented in the above described manner. There has been considerable discussion about the evolutionary status of this group; they are undoubtedly an isolated and ancient group intermediate in complexity between algae and Bryophytes.

Classification

There are many differing views concerning the status of the groups discussed above. One is that they form a single division (Chlorophyta) which may then be broken down into classes. Many authorities however place the 'euglenoid' algae and the 'charophytes' in separate divisions. The 'prasinophyte' series is new and its relationship to other green algae not yet well defined, but my own feeling is that it will eventually rank equivalent to the 'euglenoids'. A convenient scheme which cannot here be argued in detail is as follows:

Euglenophyta

    Euglenales (*Euglena, Tracheomonas, Phacus*)

    (See Leedale[3] for other orders)

Chlorophyta

    This division comprises most of the algae included in the classical schemes for the green algae but is broken down into five classes (see Round[4])

    Prasinophyceae (*Pyramimonas, Halosphaera*)

    Chlorophyceae

        Volvocales (*Chlamydomonas, Polytoma, Chlorogonium, Carteria, Haematococcus, Gonium, Pandorina, Volvox*)

        Tetrasporales (*Tetraspora*)

        Chlorococcales (*Chlorella, Chlorococcum, Scenedesmus, Pediastrum, Chodatella, Oocystis, Tetraedron, Ankistrodesmus, Kirchneriella, Crucigenia*)

        Ulotrichales (*Ulothrix*)

        Ulvales (*Ulva, Enteromorpha*)

        Chaetophorales (*Stigeoclonium, Coleochaete*)

    Oedogoniophyceae

        Oedogoniales (*Oedogonium, Bulbochaete*)

Conjugatophyceae
  Mesotaeniales. Cell wall not constricted into semicells. (*Spirotaenia, Netrium*)
  Desmidiales. Cell wall constricted into semicells. (*Closterium*—semicells indistinct, *Cosmarium, Micrasterias, Staurastrum, Xanthidium*)
  Zygnemales (*Zygnema, Mougeotia, Spirogyra*)
Bryopsidophyceae
  Cladophorales (*Cladophora*)
  Acrosiphoniales (*Urospora*)
  Siphonocladales (*Valonia*)
  Dasycladales (*Dasycladus*)
  Caulerpales (*Caulerpa*)

Charophyta
  Charophyceae
  Charales (*Chara, Nitella*)
N.B. Only the groups which have been mentioned by genus in the preceding pages are included and hence this is not a complete breakdown of the classificatory system of the Chlorophyta.

Practical Study

1. Collect all 'green algal' type growths from soil, streams, ponds, etc., and attempt to find some of the major groups. Farm ponds often yield euglenoids and other flagellate green algae.

2. Spread some material suspected to contain green algae on to 2 per cent agar in a Petri dish and observe colony formation. Do not use too much inoculum and only enough liquid to leave the agar surface moist. Remove individual colonies and transfer to liquid culture and follow development of flagellate stage.

3. If near the coast collect *Enteromorpha* and *Ulva* and place in fresh seawater. Note any formation of zoospores or gametes. Section thalli and note method of formation of holdfast.

4. Cut sections out of *Enteromorpha* and place in fresh seawater and see if any regeneration occurs. N.B. Not all species are suitable.

5. If near moorland or in regions with soft water lakes look for desmids on sediments or amongst *Sphagnum*.

6. Keep some *Spirogyra* in a jar and watch it *climb* the sides. How does it do this?

7. Design some simple experiments to show that euglenoid and volvocalean flagellates move towards the light.

8. Collect *Chara* or *Nitella* and study the vegetative morphology.

Look for reproductive stages and streaming of the chloroplasts. These genera can be maintained for years planted in soil in aquarium tanks kept filled with water.

9. Scrape the stems of reeds, etc., to remove the attached green algae. *Oedogonium, Bulbochaete* and *Coleochaete,* etc., can often be found. The latter also sometimes occurs on the undersurface and roots of duck weed (*Lemna*).

Review Questions

1. What are the 'algal' characteristics of this group?

2. How do the 'euglenoid' and 'chlamydomonad' cells differ from one another? Do you consider these differences sufficient to distinguish two divisions—compare with a clearly distinct division, e.g. the Bryophyta.

3. Discuss briefly the key features of each division and compare with features of the classes of the Chlorophyta.

4. Some workers have speculated on the origin of the Bryophyta from the green algae. What evidence can you see for this view?

5. Review the sexual reproductive mechanisms in the green algae. Since no other green lower plants have motile female gametes is there any evidence that the oogamous green algae are more advanced than the others?

6. What economic importance have the green algae?

7. Review the main features of the Conjugatophyceae. How do they differ from all other green algae? Are they paralleled by any other group of pigmented or unpigmented lower plants?

8. How far have the Charophyta advanced in morphology and reproduction towards the Bryophyta? In what ways do the two groups differ?

REFERENCES

[1] DAWSON, E. Y., *Marine Botany: An Introduction,* Holt, Rinehart & Winston, Inc., New York, 1966

[2] FRITSCH, F. E., *The Structure and Reproduction of the Algae,* Vol. I, Cambridge University Press, 1935

[3] LEEDALE, G. F., *Euglenoid Flagellates,* Prentice-Hall, Englewood Cliffs, N.J., 1967

[4] ROUND, F. E., *The Biology of the Algae,* Edward Arnold, London, 1965

[5] SMITH, G. M., *Cryptogamic Botany,* Vol. I, McGraw-Hill, New York, 1938

[6] WOLKEN, J. J., *Euglena: An Experimental Organism for Biochemical and Biophysical Studies,* Rutgers University Press, N.J., 1961

3

THE ALGAE—BROWN AND RED PIGMENTED GROUPS

SOME authorities place great stress on the distinction between green algae, the brown pigmented (Chromophyta) and the red pigmented algae (Rhodophyta). However, the groupings are partly a matter of convenience and certainly the brown pigmented group is a heterogeneous collection of groups comparable in status and diversity to those just discussed together as green algae. The Rhodophyta on the other hand are a much more circumscribed group without apparent connexions with other algal groups.

Bacillariophyta

Few algae have attracted such detailed microscopical analysis as this group and few are as widespread and abundant. The attention of microscopists has, however, concentrated on the intricate 'cell wall', which is composed of opaline silica, and much less attention has been given to the cell contents. Essentially the 'cell wall' is a box structure consisting of an upper and lower lid or valve (epitheca and hypotheca) interconnected by a series of hoops (girdle bands) (*Figures 2.1 G* and *3.1*). These girdle bands may overlap the valves or vice versa. In some genera the girdle bands are quite plain but in others pores can occur although these are generally smaller than those on the valve faces. The box may be circular (centric genera) or boat/needle shaped (pennate genera) and both types may have pores of varying complexity, arranged in intricate patterns penetrating the silica of the valves. Sometimes these are simple pores or slits, but the openings may be closed by another poroid membrane usually only visible under the electron microscope, and yet other species have a double wall with pores of different form on the outer and inner wall and also internal ribs separating the two walls.

In some pennate genera the silica wall has fissures known as raphe slits in each valve; these run between apical and median pores (*Figure 3.1 A*). Almost all forms with raphe systems are motile and it is the system of pores and raphe slits which are responsible for the diatoms' gliding movement—the details of the mechanics of this movement have fascinated biologists for over a century but are still being worked out. Some pennate forms and all centric forms are without a raphe system and none of these are actively motile.

Most diatoms are free-living unicells but a few genera form colonies, e.g. *Chaetoceros* and *Asterionella*. Many genera can attach themselves to substrata by means of mucilage pads or stalks, e.g. *Gomphonema* (*Figure 3.1*).

The cell contents are readily seen since the silica wall is perfectly transparent. The chromatophores are a rich brown colour and are either discoid, stellate or plate-like. Suspended in the centre of the cell is a diploid nucleus, and particles of a reserve polysaccharide —chrysolaminarin—may be attached to the chromatophores whilst oil globules often occur in the cytoplasm.

Mitotic division of the nucleus of the diploid vegetative cells is followed by the laying down of two new valves in membrane limited vacuoles between the two nuclei. These new valves lie back to back and they form new hypothecae (*Figure 3.1 C*)—the cells then usually split apart so that every diatom cell has one parent valve and one younger daughter valve—however, the form of these two is identical and they are usually indistinguishable. New girdle bands are then formed but as yet none of the processes have been studied in detail since the minutiae are discernible only under the electron miscroscope. At every division there is a slight reduction in length owing to the formation of the new valves inside the old and hence diatoms gradually reduce their size as they multiply. In some species this reduction in size is striking and is followed by sexual reproduction. However, there are some genera which apparently do not decrease in size during the vegetative division; this may be related to the elasticity of the walls or to the fact that it is only the girdle bands which overlap and not the valves.

Sexual reproduction in most species is a process of conjugation between cytoplasmic masses containing the nuclei. The diatoms tend to pair within mucilage clumps and each undergoes reduction division to give four nuclei in each cell. Two or three of each set of nuclei disintegrate and the remaining nuclei pair giving either one or two zygotes. In this process the parent valves have been forced apart and the zygote(s) lie free in the mucilage mass—a siliceous wall forms around the zygote nucleus and the resulting spore (auxospore) is always much larger than the parent cells. On germination a new vegetative cell forms within the auxospore wall and this is larger than the parent cells and thus reconstitutes the size of the species. One of the strange features of the diatoms is the scarcity

36

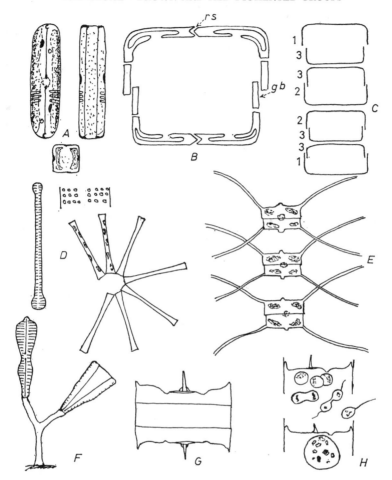

Figure 3.1. Diatoms. A, Pinnularia, *valve view showing raphe slits on left, girdle view on right and end view below;* B, *diagram of transverse section of* Pinnularia *showing chambers in silica wall and raphe slits* (rs). *Girdle bands* (gb) *very diagrammatic since it is not certain how they join with the valve;* C, *diagram of diatom cell division, oldest valves* (1,1) *and youngest* (3,3); D, *one cell of* Asterionella *in valve view, high power of part of this and colony showing cells all in girdle view;* E, *three cells of* Chaetoceros *held in a colony by the interlocking of the spines;* F, *valve and girdle view of a* Gomphonema *on a branching mucilage stalk;* G, Lithodesmium *cell;* H, *above,* Lithodesmium *cell broken open and contents cleaved and dividing to form uniflagellate gametes. Note the biflagellate stage with the flagella at either pole. Below, the contents of a cell rounding up to form an egg cell*

of observation of this sexual process and it is certain that in many species it is an extremely rare process or may even be completely lacking.

Some centric genera have an entirely different mode of sexual reproduction, involving a motile male gamete and an egg. At one time doubt was thrown on the validity of this method but recent studies have confirmed its existence in *Lithodesmium* (*Figure 3.1 G*). The egg cell is formed within a single cell by the rounding off of its contents coupled with meiosis of the nucleus. The cell producing the male gametes forms four uniflagellate gametes from each spermatocyte (normally 16 formed by cleavage of the cytoplasm) which are exceptional in that the two central fibrils are missing from the flagella.

Diatoms are extremely abundant in almost all aquatic habitats and, as anyone who has tried to culture an alga or other water plant soon discovers, the diatoms are easily cultivated. In marine habitats they are very richly developed, attached to rocks and plants in the inter-tidal and sub-tidal zone. Wherever sandy or organic sediment collects, diatoms attach to the sand grains or move over the surface of the sediments. Along ice-covered shores the diatoms grow on the undersurface of the ice. In the open sea, suspended forms abound (e.g. *Chaetoceros*) and live down to the depth to which photosynthetic usable light penetrates. Over much of the year diatoms tend to be more abundant than dinoflagellates in this planktonic habitat and without their primary fixation of carbon there would be little for the zooplankton and ultimately the fish to feed on. In brackish regions along the coasts where fresh water mixes with salt water a rich growth of species adapted to this habitat is found. Upstream where the rivers are fresh yet another series of diatom species occurs attached to stones, on sediment and particularly on aquatic Angiosperms which often appear brown from the coating of diatoms. There is little plankton in rivers except in those that are very large and slow flowing. Wherever pollution occurs the diatom flora reacts and according to the degree of pollution the number of species is reduced. In ponds and lakes the surface habitats are all colonized by diatoms and the open water supports a planktonic diatom flora, the growth of which is largely controlled by the supply of soluble silica. The soil surface abounds in diatoms and even the trunks of trees in wet tropical forests have a diatom flora.

Once the soluble silica compounds from the environment have been converted into the opaline silica of the diatom cell it is relatively indestructible except in strongly alkaline solutions; such waters are relatively rare in nature. Thus, wherever dead diatoms are deposited they tend to remain and build up appreciable depths of sediment, e.g. at the bottom of the fresh water lakes and over ocean basins. Since they are deposited in a sequence, the earliest at the bottom and the most recent at the surface, they can be utilized to supply information about past diatom floras and by deduction about past chemical and biological events in and around their sites of deposition. When these deposits are raised above lake or sea level they form valuable deposits known as diatomite which is of considerable commercial value.

Xanthophyta

Although this is a large group of algae, students may find only one genus at all common and indeed many professional botanists rarely encounter more than a handful of genera. The common genus is *Vaucheria*, transferred here from the siphonaceous green algae since it forms oil rather than starch, has auxiliary pigments characteristic of the Xanthophyta, the flagella of the male gametes are inserted laterally and those of the zoosphere are somewhat unequal (*Figure 3.2 A*). The thallus is commonly found growing on damp mud in brackish or fresh water habitats and often on soil and on plant pots in greenhouses. It has a siphonaceous growth habit with large branching threads and some colourless anchoring rhizoids—cross walls are only rarely produced, usually to delimit the antheridia and oogonia. The discoid chromatophores are green and situated in the outer lining of the cytoplasm together with the numerous nuclei. The green coloration of these algae is hardly distinguishable from that of the Chlorophyta although they have been termed the yellow-green algae. They are more readily distinguished from the Chlorophyta by the usually discoid form of the chromatophores—a rare state in the Chlorophyta except in the large and easily recognizable complex forms of the Bryopsidophyceae and the Charophyta. *Vaucheria* is unusual even amongst Xanthophyta in forming a compound zoospore (synzoospore) with numerous slightly unequal pairs of flagella (*Figure 3.2 A*). Sexual reproduction is oogamous and the antheridia and oogonia are produced adjacent to one another or on different plants. Only a single egg is formed in each oogonium—the zygote undergoes reduction division during germination so that the thallus is haploid.

Other genera are either simple filaments, e.g. *Tribonema*, or are coccoid forms often exhibiting a parallel series of morphology to those found in the Chlorococcales of the Chlorophyta. They tend, however, to form conspicuously ornamented cell walls, e.g. *Goniochloris* (*Figure 3.2 C*). A few are flagellate and these are very unequally flagellate, hence the early name of the group—Heterokontae. The very latest studies suggest that at least two series of algae are involved in this group and there is much existing work ahead for students of these genera.

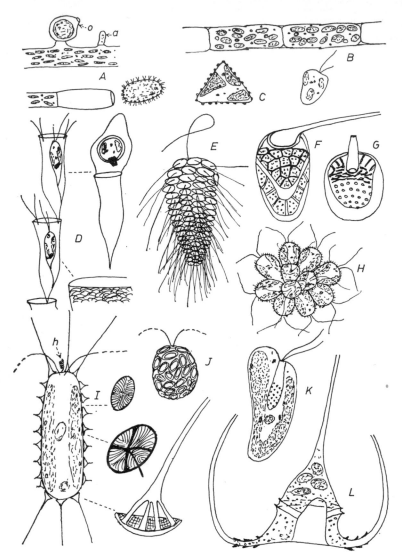

Figure 3.2. Xanthophyta, Chrysophyta, Haptophyceae, Cryptophyta and Pyrrophyta. A, Vaucheria. Above, filament with oogonium (o) and antheridium (a). Below, empty zoosporangium and synzoospore; B, Tribonema filaments and heterokont zoospore; C, Goniochloris; D, Dinobryon, two cells in thecae, characteristic spore in capsule at mouth of theca and arrangement of microfibrils in theca; E, Mallomonas; F, single scale of Mallomonas; G, scale of Synura—these latter drawn from electron microscope pictures; H, Synura colony; I, Chrysochromulina with two flagella, haptonema (h) and two types of spiny scale on body. To the right a small underscale and the two types of spiny scale as seen in electron microscope pictures; J, a coccolithophorid cell with calcareous coccoliths covering the body; K, Cryptomonas; L, Ceratium.

Chrysophyta

This is a highly characteristic group of algae with brown chromatophores, oil and leucosin as reserve substances and in some genera intricate *silica* scales coating the cells. Like the Xanthophyta they live mainly in fresh water but are much more common. The genera which are frequently found especially in the plankton are *Dinobryon* and *Mallomonas*. The former is colonial with each flagellated unicell surrounded by a microfibrillar theca (*Figure 3.2 D*) whilst the latter is free-living and covered with an armour of siliceous plates, each provided with a bristle (*Figure 3.2 E*). An unusual feature of the Chrysophyta is the variation in the number and type of flagella; in *Dinobryon* there are two unequal flagella, in *Mallomonas* a single flagellum and in *Synura* the two flagella are almost equal in length. *Synura* (*Figure 3.2 G, H*) is a colonial form with the cells arranged in a dense mass and each cell covered by numerous siliceous scales. Another striking feature is the formation of siliceous cysts within the cytoplasm, the latter passing inside the cyst and the aperture is then closed by a plug, presumably secreted from inside (*Figure 3.2 D*). Sexual reproduction has been only rarely observed.

Haptophyceae

Only recently has this very important group of algae been removed from the Chrysophyta and they will almost certainly warrant raising to the status of a division when further studies are completed. They are in many ways the marine counterparts of the Chrysophyta though a few are also found in fresh water. Included in this group are the important small flagellates known as Coccolithophorids which secrete a layer of *calcareous* plates or crystalline aggregates on to their outer surface (*Figure 3.2 J*). A second series secrete scales but these are of an unknown organic material and have been seen to form within vesicles inside the cells (*Chrysochromulina*). Both series have one further all-important characteristic, which is the possession of an additional organ, the haptonema, which occurs between the two equal flagella and is a coiled attaching organ (*Figure 3.2 I*).

Cryptophyta

Many students soon encounter this small group of mainly flagellate algae with two somewhat unequal flagella emerging from a subapical pit (*Figure 3.2 K*). They are variously pigmented often brownish

41

or olive green and occur in both fresh water and marine plankton. Small rod-like structures known as trichocysts line the subapical pit. *Cryptomonas* is very common in fresh waters, frequently living close to the sediments. Several other flagellates and even coccoid algae have been included in this group which when fully investigated may prove of considerable interest. They have been associated with the dinoflagellates by some authors but this requires further substantiation.

Pyrrophyta

Algae in this group are sometimes in the news on account of their occasional spectacular growth in tropical and subtropical waters when they colour the surface waters red—the so-called 'red tides'. No one is certain what combination of environmental factors permits such massive growth in the plankton and the problem is of economic importance since a few species manufacture a potent poison which is harmful to man but not to certain shell fish which feed on the algae. This phenomenon is recorded along the eastern coast of the United States and at such times the harvesting and eating of shell fish has to be prohibited. Other notable features of this important group are the large number of genera which are colourless and therefore more correctly considered as Protozoa, and the phenomenon of bioluminescence exhibited by some species—this involves the emission of minute flashes of light when the cells are disturbed—no other algal group has this property. The name Pyrrophyta means 'fire algae', appropriate enough for a group, some species of which produce flashes of light, and others colour the sea red. The bulk of species are flagellates living in ocean plankton but a few (probably not less than 100 species) are exclusively fresh water.

The cells are unmistakable since they have a very prominent medium furrow which divides the cells into halves, and a less conspicuous longitudinal furrow dividing the lower half when viewed from one side, but not from the other (*Figure 2.1 E*). In these two furrows are the two flagella—they arise at the junction and one runs around the median furrow and oscillates with a wave-like motion, whilst the other extends out into the water and drives the cell along. The median flagellum has a loose flagellar membrane and inside this, apart from the nine plus two system of microfibrils, a rod of unknown material extends the length of the flagellum. A further characteristic of most, possibly all, species is a rigid armour of plates joined by sutures which encloses the cytoplasm—these are often referred to as the armoured dinoflagellates, but detailed study with the electron microscope is leading to a complete reassessment of this group. It is probable that even in the forms which appear naked there is a fine outer casing which can only be seen with the electron microscope. Some genera have the wall drawn out into horns, e.g. some *Peridinium* (*Figure 2.1 E*) and *Ceratium* (*Figure 3.2 L*) species. These are the two prominent genera which are so common in samples collected with a plankton net around any coast and contribute considerably to the amount of carbon fixed in the sea. The majority of species have deep brown discoid chromatophores and a very prominent central nucleus which behaves similarly to that of *Euglena* during mitosis. They produce oil in the cells and this often has a carotenoid pigment dissolved in it—from which the red coloration of red tides is derived.

Phaeophyta (Brown seaweeds)

These are the most conspicuous of algae and most students will have already seen examples growing along rocky shores. Almost all genera are macroscopic and the largest algae known are found in two orders of the Phaeophyta—the Laminariales and Fucales. The group has been particularly successful in colonizing the shallow coastal sea and extending into the inter-tidal zone wherever there is a suitable rock to which the algae can attach. Most species have a well differentiated attaching organ (*Figures 2.1 L* and *3.4*). Very few species are free living, an exception being the floating alga, *Sargassum*, which occurs in quantity in the western Atlantic. Plants as large as the brown seaweeds grow through a series of stages and often have an alternation of gametophyte and sporophyte generations. The young stages are often delicate filamentous structures which cannot withstand the tidal movement of sand and hence the absence of the group from sandy beaches. In the past these algae were collected for the extraction of potash and iodine but now they are only used as a source of alginic acid—a substance which gels easily and has many industrial applications. Apart from some species confined to Australasia the majority of genera are widely distributed, although they are less common in tropical regions where their place in the coastal zone is taken by the siphonaceous green algae, see p. 30.

Unlike the algal groups considered so far the Phaeophyta are unusual in that there are no known vegetative flagellate or coccoid types—the simplest morphology is that of a branched filament, e.g. the common *Ectocarpus* found as tufts of brown 'hair' on larger Phaeophyta. It often grows to several centimetres in length—the filaments branch just below the cross walls and in fresh material the chromatophores are brown band-shaped structures. Material left to stand in the laboratory or preserved often has the chromatophores contracted—this is a very common occurrence in marine algae which should always be investigated as soon as possible after removal from their natural habitat. The filaments are rhizoidal at the base and in some species the whole of the lowermost part of the plant is covered in a twisting mass of 'corticating' rhizoids. The nucleus is usually quite conspicuous and around it can often be seen a cluster of vesicles—these are the fucosan vesicles containing a tannin-like substance produced by brown algae. Even a relatively simple alga such as *Ectocarpus* exhibits an alternation of generations and since both sporophyte and gametophyte are morphologically similar it is necessary to find the reproductive organs in order to determine the state of the material; in more complex Phaeophyta there is a morphological distinction. The gametophyte plants produce gametes in very characteristic swollen segments of the thallus where the cells are divided into numerous small compartments in which the gametes form—these sporangia are thus termed *plurilocular* (*Figure 3.3 B*). The gametes are pear-shaped and laterally biflagellate—the hind flagellum usually being the longer of the two. They contain plastids, mitochondria and an eyespot and this type of motile cell is common to all brown algae just as the chlamydomonad-type is to the green algae. The gametes of *Ectocarpus* fuse with apparently identical gametes from another plant—that is two strains are necessary for fusion, as in many other algae and fungi. The zygote germinates and the resulting filamentous plant differs from the gametophyte only in having the diploid number of chromosomes. On these plants small spherical/ellipsoidal sporangia replace some of the side branches—these differ from those of the gametophyte plant in that there are no cross walls, i.e. they are *unilocular* sporangia (*Figure 3.3 A*). In these the contents cleave and undergo meiotic divisions and biflagellate swarmers are formed which are released and germinate to form gametophytic plants. A further slight complication is that plurilocular sporangia may also occur on the sporophyte, but when this occurs the zooids produced in the locules are diploid and germinate into further sporophytic plants, i.e. it is merely an accessory method of vegetative propagation.

Some genera in this group of relatively simple filamentous forms are endophytic amongst the tissues of other marine algae (e.g. *Streblonema—Figure 3.3 C*)—this type of growth is not at all uncommon and when cutting sections of larger brown and red algae much of interest can be derived from a study of 'green' and 'red' algae growing on the surface or between the cells of the host plant. Other representatives of the Ectocarpales form crust-like growths owing to the aggregation of upright filaments into an almost parenchymatous mass, e.g. *Ralfsia (Figure 3.3 D)*.

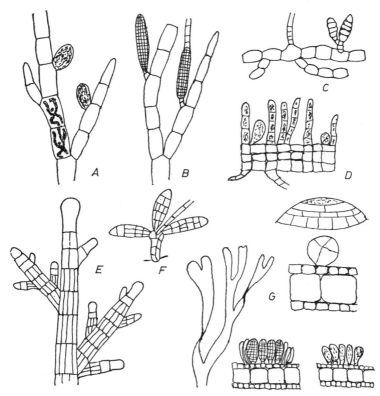

Figure 3.3. Phaeophyta. A, Ectocarpus *with unilocular sporangia; B,* Ectocarpus *with plurilocular sporangia; C,* Streblonema; *D,* Ralfsia; *E,* Sphacelaria; *F, propagule of* Sphacelaria; *G,* Dictyota. *Plant, apex and sections of thallus showing a tetrasporangium; below left antheridia and right oogonia*

The Phaeophyta have been arranged by taxonomists in a series starting with simple filamentous types such as *Ectocarpus*, continuing with those of increasing complexity and culminating in the highly differentiated *Laminaria* and *Fucus*. Linked with this elaboration of the thallus is a localization of the meristematic sites, well defined life histories and form of gametangia. One of the simplest is *Sphacelaria (Figure 3.3 E)* which is easily found growing on larger algae in rock pools in the inter-tidal zone. It is perhaps the most striking of plants with single apical cells at each branch end. These cut off cells to the base which then undergo longitudinal division so that in the older parts the thallus is a solid rod of cells. A precise mechanism is also present controlling the development of the pinnate side branches which in some species are formed in a single plane and strictly from alternate cells cut off from the apical cell. Towards the base of the plant, corticating (i.e. clothing the main axis) filaments grow downwards and over the original holdfast. Unilocular and plurilocular sporangia are formed on the isomorphic generations as in *Ectocarpus*, but more frequently encountered are the characteristic vegetative propagules (*Figure 3.3 F*) which drop off the plant and germinate. Another brown alga with a conspicuous apical cell is *Dictyota*, found growing on wet rock faces in the lower inter-tidal of temperate zones and very abundant in tropical waters. The apical cell is again a prominent feature; it is an ideal subject to demonstrate apical dichotomy. The subsequent divisions of cells are less easy to follow but careful focusing through the thallus will reveal that there is an outer layer of small cells packed with chromatophores and internally just one layer of large cells (*Figure 3.3 G*). The flat, dichotomizing thalli often have small dark patches on the surface, these may be either groups of oogonia, antheridia or tetraspores depending upon the nature of the plant—morphologically they are identical but in fact three separate plants are involved. The reproductive organs are best seen in transverse sections (*Figure 3.3 G*)—the oogonial groups or sori produce single, non-motile egg cells from each oogonium, whilst the antheridia produce numerous antherozooids which are unusual in having only a single flagellum (there is in fact a vestigial second flagellum, obvious only in sections cut for investigation under the electron microscope). The tetraspore clusters are as their name suggests groups of 4 spores, being the products of meiosis in the 'unilocular' sporangia formed on the sporophyte plant. These plants form a very elegant example of the alternation of isomorphic generations with dioecious gametophytes and non-motile spores formed in tetrasporangia—this is a state which is common in the final group of algae—the red algae (p. 51), but not quite so easy to observe in that very complex group.

Plants in which growth is more diffuse and the thallus is virtually parenchymatous coupled with a pronounced *heteromorphic* alternation of generations are characteristic of the Dictyosiphonales. *Scytosiphon* is a readily recognizable genus of this group (*Figure 3.4 A*)—its articulated tubular thalli (up to 20 cm in length) frequent rock pools and wet rock surfaces in the inter-tidal zone, growing on the rock and often on limpet shells. One of the fascinating but also frustrating aspects of studying brown algae is linking up the gametophytes and sporophytes of a single genus—this is very difficult to do in the natural habitat but now that many species can be cultivated it is proving easier. However, the life histories of many species have still not been completely investigated and *Scytosiphon* is one which has still not been completely clarified, though recently it has been shown that the tubular *Scytosiphon* plants are gameto-phytic and alternate with a creeping filamentous sporophyte (*Figure 3.4 A*).

Even more pronounced is the alternation between the massive kelps of the Laminariales and their minute filamentous game-tophytes. These gametophytes are sparsely branched and presum-ably grow on and in cracks of rocks in the sub-tidal zone—the female plants have slightly larger cells than the male and form single non-motile egg cells in terminal sporangia. The male plants form small clusters of antheridia, each cell of which produces a typically phaeophycean gamete (*Figure 3.4 F*). The eggs are extruded from the oogonium but remain attached to the broken oogonial wall, are fertilized *in situ* and develop to small sporophytic plants whilst still attached to the gametophytes (*Figure 3.4 G*). The young plants are minute leaf-like structures of parenchymatous tissue—soon the meristematic activity begins to define a holdfast, stipe and blade and as growth proceeds the main meristematic region becomes located at the junction of stipe and blade, although the outer layer of assimilatory cells continues to divide. Transverse and longitudinal sections of stipes and laminae reveal a fairly complex arrangement of tissues (*Figure 3.4 H*)—the outermost layer of cubical cells divides and provides some cells to the cortex, which consists of oblong cells becoming more filamentous towards the central medulla region; here there is copious production of mucilage. Some of the elongate cells of the inner cortex form papillae which fuse with those of adjacent cells and grow to form the cross connexions (*Figure 3.4 K*) some of which traverse the medulla. Other cells develop into long hyphal-like growths which become constricted longitudinally in the central region—in some genera the end walls of these cells forming the hyphae develop perforations and appear as 'sieve plates'. The stretching of the hyphae between these 'sieve plates' gives a characteristic form, hence the term 'trumpet hyphae' (*Figure 3.4 I, J*). Unilocular sporangia form from the surface cells of the thallus and are protected by palisade-like paraphyses growing between and extending beyond the sporangia. In some genera they are confined to special regions of the blade and/or laminae and

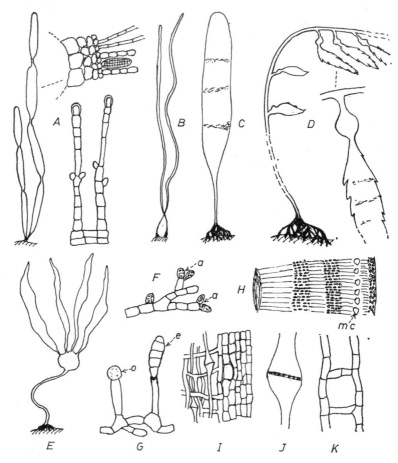

Figure 3.4. Phaeophyta. A, plant of Scytosiphon and on right transverse section of thallus showing hairs and plurilocular sporangia. Below, a fragment of the alternate stage of Scytosiphon; B, Chorda; C, Laminaria; D, portion of a Macrocystis plant and part of one lamina showing the basal air bladder; E, Nereocystis; F, male plant of a 'laminarian' with antheridia (a); G, female plant of a 'laminarian' with egg cell (o) and young embryo plant (e); H, part of transverse section of stipe of Laminaria showing 'growth rings' and mucilage canals (mc); I, longitudinal section of a Laminaria stipe; J, the 'sieve plate' region of a trumpet hypha; K, cross-connexions of the filaments from the medulla of a 'laminarian'

in some to special outgrowths—sporophylls, e.g. *Alaria (Figure 2.1 L)*. The simplest morphology is that of *Chorda*, which forms a thin cylindrical whip-like thallus; *Laminaria* has a relatively simple flattened blade whilst *Alaria* is similar but with a mid-rib, thinner wings and 'pods' growing out of the stipe bearing the unilocular sporangia. Some genera differentiate large air-bladders, which serve to buoy the photosynthetic blades up to the surface, e.g. in *Nereocystis* (*Figure 3.4 E*) the bladder at the top of the stipe may be twice the size of a tennis ball and from this the long blades stream out into the water. The commercially valuable *Macrocystis* (*Figure 3.4 D*) has a small bladder at the base of each blade, whilst the holdfast can develop into a massive structure a metre or more in diameter.

The Laminariales are important compounds of the sub-tidal flora in cold regions and in cold currents. They extend upwards only into the lowermost region of the inter-tidal zone and hence it is only by diving that the full extent of the *Laminaria* forest can be appreciated.

Most students will be familiar with the general morphology of the final group, the Fucales, whilst new forms are readily recognizable when fruiting since they all have the gametangia embedded in pits usually localized on the thallus. In north temperate zones they tend to be common inter-tidal plants of rocky shores, but there are a group of Australasian species which are more commonly found in the sub-tidal zone and the genus *Sargassum* (*Figure 3.5 F*) has free-floating species. They have a very characteristic rather monotonous life-history which sets them apart from all other brown algae. Meiosis occurs in the gametangia prior to the formation of gametes, as in most animals, and all spore stages have been eliminated. Thus we only have to consider the sporophyte plant since the haploid phase is confined to the gametes. The sporophytes exhibit a wide range of morphology, but basically there is a radial organization seen in *Sargassum* and *Cystoseira* (*Figure 3.5 H*) and a bilateral symmetry with dichotomous branching as in *Pelvetia* and *Fucus* (*Figure 3.5 A* and *B*). In the former the holdfast and stipe give rise to numerous branches which have a petiole and leaf-like blade complete with venation. They form small branches bearing air-bladders, and other twig-like branches bearing the receptacles. Mature *Fucus* plants are again divisible into holdfast (almost always disc-like in the Fucales as opposed to the branching type common in the Laminariales) stipe and blade with a central mid-rib. Air bladders occur in some species and swollen branch tips either bear sterile pits (cryptostomata—also formed all over the thallus in some genera) or fertile pits (conceptacles). Growth is by means of single apical cells embedded in cavities at the tips of the branches (*Figure 3.5 I*). Although not as complex as in *Laminaria* the thallus is composed of meristoderm, cortex and medulla showing hyphal extension of the cells. The fertile conceptacles produce antheridia on the paraphyses, which radiate into the centre of the cavity, and oogonia on short single cells growing from the basal cells of the conceptacle (*Figure 3.5 J*). This arrangement is fairly uniform in the group though

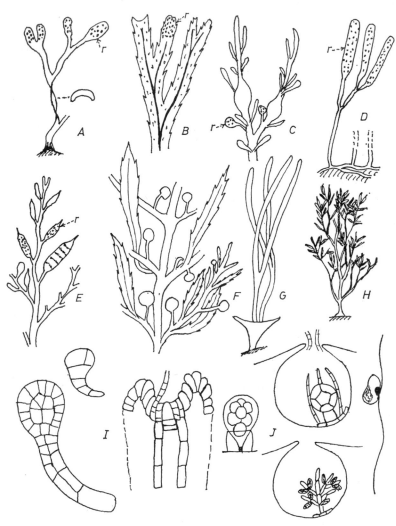

Figure 3.5. Phaeophyta—Fucales. A, Pelvetia, *with fertile tips* (*r—in this and others*)*; B*, Fucus; *C*, Ascophyllum; *D*, Bifurcaria; *E*, Halidrys; *F*, Sargassum; *G*, Himanthalia; *H*, Cystoseira; *I, growth of embryo 'fucoid' and on right apical cell; J, fertile conceptacles—oogonia above and antheridia below. Release of eggs on left and spermatozooid on right*

antheridia and oogonia may be in the same conceptacle, in different conceptacles or on different plants. The number of eggs in the oogonia vary from one to eight. Male conceptacles are often recognizable from the orange coloration of the fertile portion of the thallus. This is caused by the excess of carotenoid pigments in the spermatozooids.

Ecologically the Fucoids are important constituents of the various vertical bands recognizable on rocky shores in Europe; *Pelvetia* occurs at the top of the shore followed by *Fucus spiralis*, then *F. vesiculosus* and *Ascophyllum nodosum*, whilst *F. serratus* tends to be lowest on the shore. *Himanthalia elongata (Figure 3.5 G)* is a striking Fucoid which occurs around low tide level, whilst *Halidrys, Bifurcaria* and *Cystoseira* grow in rock pools in the inter-tidal zone. These are merely general comments on zonation, and varying degrees of wave action, exposure, rock substrate, morphology of shore, etc., impart an individual stamp to every site.

Rhodophyta

With at least 4000 species this is the second largest group of the algae and although a considerable number of forms have been recorded in fresh water more than 95 per cent are marine where they grow extensively in the inter-tidal and particularly sub-tidal zones. A small number of species are unicellular but the vast majority are branched filamentous structures—sometimes the filaments are relatively simple, e.g. *Achrochaetium (Figure 3.6 B)* but more often they have complex corticating systems and in many the filaments are aggregated to form pseudoparenchyma. In this group calcification of the thallus reaches its highest development amongst any group of plants, with over 400 species of 'coralline' algae—many so calcified as to be mistaken for corals or lumps of rock. The metabolism of these algae exhibits some special features, e.g. the presence of accessory phycobilin pigments (phycoerythrin and phycocyanin in the chromatophores) and in the production of various mucilages some of which are sulphated polysaccharides found only in this group. Lastly but certainly not least their reproductive processes never involve flagellated cells and their female organs and life cycles are the most intriguing and complicated in the whole of the plant kingdom. In many genera there are male and female plants and tetraspore plants, all morphologically similar as in the brown alga *Dictyota*.

The red algae have long been divided into two sections, of which the first, the Bangiophycidae, is the simplest. Most students will only meet the deep purplish red 'laver', *Porphyra* (*Figure 3.6 A*) which grows in the upper part of rocky shores and looks rather like a thin purple coloured lettuce leaf attached to the rocks. The life histories of these plants have proved extremely difficult to investigate but a Japanese species which is cultivated on a large scale for food has been fairly extensively studied. There is an alternation of the *Porphyra* plant with a filamentous '*Conchocelis*' plant usually found growing in mollusc shells. Spores are produced on both stages but many aspects of the life history are still unknown. The few genera in this section are either relatively simple unicells, filaments or flat thalli without pits connecting the cells.

On the other hand the second group, Florideophycidae, containing all the well known red-algal genera, although basically filamentous exhibit an immense diversity of form from branched filaments (e.g. *Achrochaetium* or *Batrachospermum, Figure 3.6 D*) to *Delesseria* with its stem and leaves (*Figure 3.6 F*). Branched filamentous genera occur in most orders but are difficult to classify unless they bear reproductive structures; sometimes the type of branching is characteristic and the presence or absence of corticating filaments can be utilized. In the morphologically more complex genera, e.g. *Dumontia*, which is often found in rock pools, a central filament is dominant and side branches give rise to smaller laterals which aggregate to form an outer pseudoparenchymatous skin (*Figure 3.6 C*)—the internal spaces between the cells often become filled with characteristic jelly-like substances. In other genera there are many axial filaments each with an apical cell and giving rise to lateral branches—an easily investigated alga of this type is *Corallina*. This also illustrates calcification of the thallus, whilst it is one of the commonest algae of rock pools. The pinkish thalli are composed of articulated segments (*Figure 3.6 E*) and for investigating the thallus it is best to decalcify the plant in dilute hydrochloric acid and then wash well before mounting on a slide. In the regions between the swollen segments the large number of axial filaments can be seen. Whenever a red alga is available its structure should be determined since this is the only way to appreciate the branching systems involved—this is not an easy task and some are so complex that they will seem impossible, but others, such as the 'leafy' forms, can be understood if the apices are studied. Thus *Delesseria* can be seen to consist of an axial row of cells giving off elongated laterals (*Figure 3.6 F*); the thick mid-rib region is derived from laterals cut off in a plane at right angles to the lamina.

Many Rhodophyta, and particularly the sub-tidal forms, are readily recognizable from the pink to deep red coloration, but

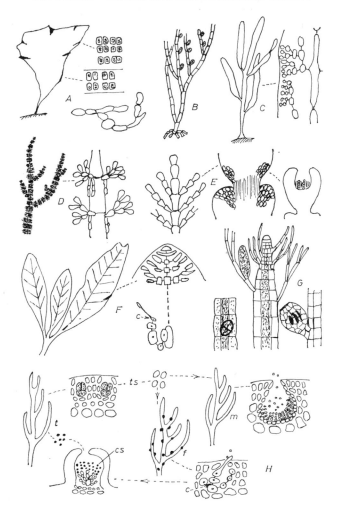

Figure 3.6. Rhodophyta. A, Porphyra *plant, surface view and section of thallus on right and below a fragment of the* Conchocelis *phase; B,* Acrochaetium; *C,* Dumontia *plant and part of longitudinal section of the thallus showing the axial filament; D, fragment of* Batrachospermum *and on right the branch and cortication system; E,* Corallina. *Apex of plant, 'node' showing multiaxial system and far right a 'tetraspore' conceptacle; F,* Delesseria, *plant, apical segmentation and carpogonial branch with carpogonium (c); G,* Polysiphonia, *apex of plant with branched hairs and antheridium, on left a tetraspore within the thallus and on right a cystocarp containing carpospores; H, the life cycle of* Gracilaria. *'Tetraspore' plant (t) and tetraspores (ts). Male plant (m) with section through spermatial pit. Female plant (f) and section through thallus showing carpogonial branch (c) and to left a cystocarp with carpospores (cs)*

many of the inter-tidal species are a rich brown colour whilst the fresh water forms are a greyish-green colour; thus the student is often led into the wrong group. The chromatophores are usually simple—stellate in the Bangiophycideae and discoid or often elongated into long strands in the Florideophycideae—little else is visible of diagnostic value in the red algal cells.

The simplest part of the reproductive cycle is the production of the male cells (spermatia)—these are non-motile cells each formed in a single cell cut off from a branching filament. In some genera they are formed within pits in the thalli, e.g. *Gracilaria (Figure 3.6 H)*. The female plants bear the female organs in a truly 'cryptogamic' manner, hidden in the cortical tissues of the thallus, and it is usually only by sectioning that they become obvious. They are oogamous and the egg cell is retained in the specialized oogonium—here called the carpogonium *(Figure 3.6 F, H)*. The latter is drawn out into a long neck or trichogyne, the tip of which penetrates to the outside between the superficial tissues. The carpogonium itself is borne on a special branch system arising from a cortical cell and growing in the mucilage between the cortical cells. A spermatium sticks to the trichogyne, is absorbed and transferred down into the carpogonium where the nuclei fuse to form the zygote. It is the next stage which is unexpected, for in many genera the diploid nucleus of the zygote is transferred via a filament which grows out from the carpogonium to make contact and then fuse with other cortical cells leaving a diploid nucleus behind in each cell which is contacted—the diploid nucleus divides by mitotis during this process. In other genera the diploid nucleus is merely passed to a cell of the branch bearing the carpogonium by fusion between the carpogonium and one cell of the branch. There are very many variations in the arrangement of the carpogonial branch and the subsequent transference of the diploid nucleus, and unfortunately it is this system which is used in the taxonomic grouping of the red algae into orders. The cell either of the carpogonial branch or within the cortex to which a diploid nucleus has been transferred gives rise to a series of filaments from which arise rows of single celled *diploid* spores—the carpospores. At this stage the carpogonial branch is usually no longer recognizable and the tissues around the carpospore-producing site often enlarge and the whole structure is termed the cystocarp *(Figure 3.6 G, H)*. The whole diploid structure growing from the zygote and retained on the haploid female plant is generally called the carposporophyte. The diploid carpospores are released, germinate and grow into a new plant usually identical in form to the gametophyte but of diploid status and referred to as the tetraspore plant. Within the cortex of this plant and often in special proliferations certain cells undergo meoisis to yield the tetraspores, two of which produce male plants and two female (*Figure 3.6 E, H*). The above account is merely a very brief generalized summary and for further details specialized monographs must be consulted.

Classification

The Rhodophyta, with no flagellate stage (Aconta), special pigments, and the complex arrangement of the carpogonium and its post fertilization changes are clearly an entirely self-contained group.

Rhodophyta
  Rhodophyceae
    Bangiophycidae
      Bangiales (*Porphyra*)
    Florideophycidae
      Nemalionales (*Acrochaetium, Batrachospermum*)
      Cryptonemiales (*Corallina, Dumontia*)
      Gigartinales (*Gracilaria*)
      Ceramiales (*Ceramium, Delesseria, Polysiphonia*)

The aggregate of algal groups, which has been termed Chromophyta by some authorities, are, in the author's opinion better kept as separate divisions and the term 'chromophyta' used when a general reference to brown pigmented algae is required.

Bacillariophyta (Diatoms)
    Centrales (*Stephanodiscus, Chaetoceros, Lithodesmium*)
    Pennales (*Asterionella, Pinnularia, Gomphonema*)

Xanthophyta (Heterocontae)
    Heterococcales (*Goniochloris*)
    Heterotrichales (*Tribonema*)
    Heterosiphonales (*Vaucheria*)

Chrysophyta
    Chrysomonadales (*Dinobryon, Mallomonas, Synura*)

Haptophyceae
    Prymnesiales (*Chrysochromulina, Coccolithophorids*)

Pyrrophyta (Dinoflagellates)
  There are two classes. Desmophyceae and Dinophyceae—the

former are quite common marine flagellates in which the theca is composed of two watch-glass like halves.

Dinophyceae
    Peridiniales (*Peridinium, Ceratium*)

Cryptophyta
    Cryptomonadales (*Cryptomonas*)

There is probably little virtue in not giving the Haptophyceae the status of a division, especially now that many authors consider each other group a division.

Finally there is the large division, Phaeophyta, which in concept is more like the Chlorophyta, including several quite distinct series of brown algae, some of which have been grouped into sub-classes based on life cycles.

Phaeophyta
    Ectocarpales (*Ectocarpus, Streblonema, Ralfsia*)
    Sphacelariales (*Sphacelaria*)
    Dictyotales (*Dictyota*)
    Dictyosiphonales (*Scytosiphon*)
    Laminariales (*Alaria, Chorda, Laminaria, Macrocystis, Nereocystis*)
    Fucales (*Ascophyllum, Bifurcaria, Cystoseira, Fucus, Halidrys, Himanthalia, Pelvetia, Sargassum*)

As in the 'chlorophyte' series there are several other orders which have not been mentioned in this introductory account.

Practical Study

1. Collect material from patches of sediment which appear brown in ponds, streams, rock pools, etc. One soon begins to recognize these patches of diatom growth. Also scrape the stems of water plants, seaweeds, stones in streams, etc., and rich collections of diatoms will usually be found. Illustrate some representative forms and familiarize yourself with this extremely widespread and abundant group.

2. Spread some of the material containing diatoms on agar plates or put into culture solution and see how readily they grow.

3. Take some rich diatom material and 'clean' by boiling in dilute hydrogen peroxide. Mount some of the residue by drying a drop on a coverglass and then mounting this in Canada Balsam. The cells will split apart and the girdle bands will also be revealed. Use the oil immersion objective to see detail of pores, raphe systems, etc.

4. Whenever you find other algae of these groups, e.g. *Peridinum, Cryptomonas, Dinobryon,* make as many observations as you can on them, illustrate them and compare with the above discussion. They are not uncommon but it is not easy to quote a guaranteed method to collect them. If you have access to a plankton net then you will certainly be able to collect some either in fresh water or along the coast.

5. The brown seaweeds are in some ways the most difficult to study. Try to start with filamentous genera collected off larger seaweeds. Always try to obtain the bases of the plants so that you can investigate the attachment system. Look for sporangia and try to decide how the plant grows whether by apical cells or intercalary meristems.

6. Collect material of *Laminaria* species either at low tide on rocky coasts or washed up in the drift on the shore. Cut sections of the stipe and lamina using a razor or razor blade.

7. Look for fertile plants of the Fucales. Cut sections of the fertile regions and look for antheridia and oogonia. If you find section cutting difficult, then it is surprising what good results can sometimes be achieved by chopping small pieces of thallus on a slide with a razor blade as though you were chopping parsley.

8. A wealth of Rhodophyta can be found growing on rocky shores or washed up in the drift. *Corallina* species and others coated with calcium carbonate require decalcifying in dilute hydrochloric acid. (N.B. Wash well before putting under the microscope.) Always look for young apices and try to work out the sequence of cell division. Cross-sections are often valuable and the chopping technique is useful here. Look especially for *Polysiphonia* plants which yield good apical cells and are frequently fertile. Look for fertile stages of others but do not be put off if you cannot find them —many professional botanists have never seen them.

9. If near a rocky shore spend a little time noting the zonation of the larger algae. The fact that you will not be able to name all the algae need not deter you since the general features of zonation will be obvious.

10. See how many algae you can find growing in or on others and also in and on animals (e.g. freshwater snails, limpets).

Review Questions

1. Diatoms and desmids are both fairly complex unicells. Have they any features in common or do they differ completely? Compare the sexual reproduction of the two groups.

2. Diatom 'cell walls' are composed of silica. Where does this come from—consult the geologists and geographers? What happens to it after death of the diatom cells? What other plant or animal groups use silica to form skeletons.

3. How many kinds of flagellated cells occur in the 'chromophyte' grouping of algae? How do these differ from those in the 'chlorophyte' series?

4. What are the identifying characteristics of the Phaeophyta? How does this group compare in vegetative and reproductive range with the 'chlorophyte' group?

5. Which algal group or genus would you regard as the most complex? Is this nearest to the simplest present day Bryophyta? Does there appear to be any reason why brown or red algae have not given rise to archegoniate plant groups?

6. The Phaeophyta and Rhodophyta have exploited the filamentous plant form to its utmost. Show how this has been achieved. How is it related to meristematic activity?

7. Review the mechanisms of sexual reproduction in Phaeophyta and Rhodophyta. In what ways are these conservative systems?

8. Algae as a whole appear to be a highly successful group, adapting to fill a multitude of habitats. What are these habitats and what are the major algal groups to be found in each?

BIBLIOGRAPHY

Boney, A. D., *A Biology of Marine Algae*, Hutchinson Educational Ltd., London, 1966

Dawson, E. Y., *Marine Botany. An Introduction*, Holt, Rinehart & Winston, New York, 1966

Fritsch, F. E., *The Structure and Reproduction of the Algae*, Vols. 1 and 2, Cambridge University Press, 1935, 1945

Lewis, J. R., *The Ecology of Rocky Shores*, English Universities Press, London, 1964

Round, F. E., *The Biology of the Algae*, Edward Arnold, London, 1965

Smith, G. M., *Cryptogamic Botany*, Vol. 1, McGraw-Hill, New York, 1938

4

THE FUNGI—INTRODUCTION AND PHYCOMYCETE GROUPS

MOST groups of lower plants are active in the fixation of carbon and the building up of more complex molecules whilst few perform the equally vital breakdown of organic matter; without this latter process the land and water would rapidly become choked with material which could only be decomposed slowly by chemical processes. Whilst bacteria tend to invade any material as soon as it dies or is damaged in any way, the fungi, because they are larger and slower growing, are often secondary invaders though in some instances they penetrate healthy organisms, e.g. the parasitic chytrids which infect many algal species. Saprophytic fungi, i.e. those growing on dead material, are more numerous, e.g. the fungal 'mould' which grows on exposed foods. In nature there is a complex interweaving mass of fungal hyphae and unicellular species occurring in all soils, humus, lake and sea bed deposits, whilst fungal spores or fragments are floating in both fresh water, salt water and in the air. It is questionable whether a single plant or animal, including man, can be found in nature without fungal thalli of some sort growing on or within the body. Anyone who doubts their ubiquity has only to leave Petri dishes containing agar open for a few minutes and examine the consequences a few days later—the same experiments can be done with table jelly!

All fungi are collected together into a single division of the plant kingdom—Mycota—they are basically coenocytic and unicellular organisms although proliferation of the coenocytes and formation of cross walls occur in certain groups. A few are simple spherical structures but the majority form thin branching hyphae, and although in some genera cross partitions are formed to delimit segments of hyphae these have a central pore through which the cytoplasm passes. It is only in the formation of spores that segments of the cytoplasm become delimited by walls. The wall material is either cellulose or more frequently chitin. Hyphae are really long thin siphonaceous structures growing by extension of the apices and the formation of more cytoplasm and nuclei. The hyphae branch repeatedly and the mass of threads thus formed is termed the mycelium; in many fungi this packs together to form macroscopic strands and also the complex fruiting bodies (sporophores). Although there are no photosynthetic pigments it is not correct to think of fungi as unpigmented since many species produce carotenoids which give rise to a range of colours from yellow to red and even blue. The products of metabolism which accumulate in the cytoplasm are fat and glycogen.

Asexual reproduction is very common and results in the rapid spread of fungi. Flagellate zoospores are formed in the groups regarded as the most primitive and aplanospores in the other groups —these are formed within sporangia (sporangiospores) or as external, often thick walled cells (conidia) on special hyphal structures —conidiophores. Hyphae may fragment into unthickened sections —oidia, or into thick-walled fragments—chlamydospores.

Sexual reproduction may involve isogamy, anisogamy or oogamy in a manner comparable to that of many algae. However, in most of the higher terrestrial fungi, plasmogamy, which is the fusion of small masses of cytoplasm containing the nuclei, is separated in time from karyogamy, which is the fusion of the nuclei to form a zygote. The nuclei from the two parents may co-exist side by side in the hypha for a considerable time, forming what is known as a dikaryon; during this time the two nuclei may divide many times before the final fusion.

The growth of fungi impinges upon man more strikingly than that of any other group of lower plants. Mushrooms and other fungi are eaten by man and now are cultivated for sale, but fungi also grow on man and domestic animals causing mycoses, of which probably the commonest is 'athletes foot'. Gardeners and farmers are well aware of the detrimental effects of fungal diseases on plants which cause tremendous damage to crops, and have been so severe in the past as to effect the migration of man from one continent to another—over two million Irish being driven to N. America during the last century by the starvation caused by fungal diseases of potatoes. Alongside this and of even greater biological importance is the steady breakdown of organic compounds and particularly of cellulose and lignin which otherwise would decay very slowly. Finally in many societies the growth of fungi in liquids is the basis of the brewing industry, but is also used in cheese making, baking, production of alcohols, organic acids and complex molecules such as the antibiotics.

The fungi have long been divided into three large sections based on morphology of the thallus and on reproductive characters. The classical groups are Phycomycetes; mainly non-septate forms with a variety of reproductive cells, flagellate and aplanate; Ascomycetes and Basidiomycetes form septa and in the former the products of meiosis are formed endogenously in a sporangium known as the ascus, whilst the Basidiomycetes form their spores exogenously on a special structure, the basidium. These are still convenient assemblages and in the two latter, although many taxonomic changes have been made the old concepts of the groups stand. The Phycomycetes, however, are recognized as a diverse assemblage of fungi and they have been split into a series of classes from Chytridiomycetes to Trichomycetes and these classes will be used from now on, although some can only be mentioned briefly. It is interesting that exactly the same situation exists in the algae where the most advanced groups (Phaeophyta and Rhodophyta) have merely required internal reorganization, whereas the 'chlorophyte' series has been split up. Parts of the 'phycomycete' series may indeed merely be 'colourless' algae. This concept was aired many decades ago but only recently have electron microscope studies reaffirmed the argument.

Chytridiomycetes

These fungi are the only ones in the Mycota which possess motile cells with a single *posterior* flagellum which is naked—that is, there are no fine strands radiating out from the flagellar sheath when seen in preparations studied under the electron microscope. The chytrids (Chytridiales) have the simplest thallus within this class—it is a simple sac-like structure produced from germination of a zoospore. In some genera fine rhizoidal threads also develop but these seem to be subsidiary to the main mass of the thallus and do not contain nuclei. Many species are aquatic (e.g. *Chytridium, Figure 4.1 A*) and parasitize algae to such an extent that they can alter the balance of the populations. Others are saprophytic on plant and animal substrates in water and soils. Some have not yet been grown in culture but an increasing number are yielding to modern techniques. A few genera are parasitic, causing diseases such as potato wart disease. *Synchytrium endobioticum* (*Figure 4.2 B*) is the causative chytrid.

Reproductive cycles have been determined for some but not all chytrids. The simpler genera are holocarpic, that is the whole parent thallus is converted into reproductive units, either zoospores or planogametes—the two are usually indistinguishable except in function. Thus in *Olpidium* (*Figure 4.2 A*) the germ tube from the zoospore penetrates the host, and then swells into the chytrid thallus

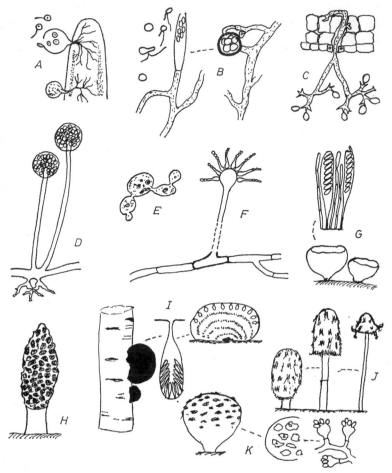

Figure 4.1. The range of fungi. A, a chytrid (Chytridum) *parasitic on an alga. Cells epibiotic with mycelium penetrating the alga, and one converted into a sporangium opening by means of a 'cap', releasing posteriorly uniflagellate swarmers; B,* Saprolegnia. *Plant on left with zoosporangium and swarmers of two different types. Plant on right with oospheres in the oogonium and branched antheridium penetrating the oogonium; C, a fragment of* Plasmopara *emerging through a stoma and giving rise to conidia; D,* Rhizopus—*two sporangia and hyphal branches growing downwards from a stolon; E, a budding yeast,* Saccharomyces; *F, a conidiophore of* Aspergillus *arising from a thickened 'foot cell'; G, two apothecia of* Peziza, *and above, two asci containing eight ascospores; H, the fruit body of the ascomycete* Morchella; *I, a twig with two black fruit bodies of* Daldinia. *On the right a section through the fruit body showing 'growth rings' and perithecia and a single perithecium; J, three fruit bodies (sporophores) of* Coprinus *in varying stages of maturity; K, fruit body of* Scleroderma: *on right a section showing cavities in which the basidia form, and on far right the basidia bearing basidiospores*

within the host cell. The formation of a thick wall converts the thallus into a sporangium which releases zoospores to repeat the cycle. At times the 'planospores' act as gametes and the zygote then penetrates the host cell, and after formation of a thallus becomes completely converted into a thick-walled sporangium ultimately releasing zoospores and presumably completing meiosis during their formation. *Synchytrium* differs only in detail from this basic cycle.

A somewhat more elaborate thallus characterizes *Allomyces* (*Figure 4.2 C*) of the Blastocladiales—the hyphae are branched and thickening of the wall gives the appearance of septation. The sporophyte thallus forms thin-walled or thick-walled sporangia— the former produce zoospores which are diploid and germinate to perpetuate the sporophyte, whilst within the thick-walled sporangia meiosis gives rise to haploid zoospores. These on germination grow into small gametophytes which form male and female gametangia adjacent to one another, apparently replacing side branches. The male gametangia are the smaller and are recognizable from the carotenoid pigment which is formed and apportioned to the gametes. This genus in anisogametic—the female gametes being the larger.

A final small order, the Monoblepharidales, establishes a more 'fungal' type of organization in this primitive class. A characteristic fungal mycelium occurs in the aquatic *Monoblepharis* (*Figure 4.2 D*) and is here distinguished by a foamy, vacuolate state of the cytoplasm—the tips of the hyphae are cut off by cross walls to form elongate but otherwise undifferentiated sporangia, producing posteriorly uniflagellate zoospores which germinate to form further mycelium. On this same thallus, oogonia form as swollen segments near the apex and antheridia as small cylindrical appendages on the oogonium. The egg cell is non-motile but the antheridium produces antherozooids of the normal, posteriorly flagellate type. After fusion the zygote escapes through a pore in the oogonium and there encysts to form an ornamented oospore which ultimately germinates with the formation not of zoospores but of a germ tube as in higher fungi.

Plasmodiophoromycetes

Scattered throughout the lower plants are groups of uncertain affinities. The single order Plasmodiophorales has at times been associated with the slime moulds (Myxomycetes) but it certainly possesses too many distinct characteristics to remain there. The species also form unequally biflagellate swarmers and gametes, but no cell wall around the cytoplasm. The common *Plasmodiophora brassicae* is an endoparasite which lives in the cells of host plants of the Angiosperm group Cruciferae—it causes the disease 'club root' of cultivated *Brassica* spp. such as cabbage, turnip, etc. The plasmodia within the cells cause a swelling of the root tissues and general disruption of the conducting system; these plasmodia form resting spores within the cells and in this way the disease is transmitted since fragments of tissue and spores released from them remain in the soil. The life-cycle of *Plasmodiophora* is complex and not all the details have been verified. The spores release biflagellate swarmers which then lose their flagella but continue to move in an amoeboid manner and finally infect plants through the root hairs. Inside the hosts the plasmodium divides and this is thought to produce gametangia, since the resulting biflagellate cells act as gametes on release into the soil. The zygotes reinfect the host plants and form a plasmodium which can penetrate the host cell walls and proliferate through the cells.

Oomycetes

As the name of the class implies all these fungi form non-motile egg cells. In addition, the zygotes develop into oospores *within* the oogonia; the antheridia penetrate the oogonia directly and thus a highly active motile stage is unnecessary; only in asexual reproduction are motile biflagellate swarmers produced. The cell walls are composed of cellulose. Within the group there is a series ranging from simple aquatic types to terrestrial obligate parasites of considerable economic importance. Some aquatic species are readily cultivated by hanging bait such as fruits, seeds, etc., in water or by bringing the water into the laboratory and 'baiting' it in Petri dishes. The parasitic species are often found amongst seedlings grown under too crowded conditions and also as white powdery growths on common plants—though here it is necessary to identify the material carefully since other fungi can form rather similar looking growths—however, the spore types are quite characteristic.

Two small orders of aquatic fungi, the Lagenidiales and Leptomitales, will not be considered in detail. The former (*Figure 4.2 E*) produce branching colonies within algae and other aquatic organisms—the sporangia penetrate the cell wall to the outside and release biflagellate zoospores which reinfect. Antheridia and oogonia are also formed within the host cells and the antheridium passes a small tube through the oogonial wall prior to fertilization. The resting oospore eventually releases biflagellate zoospores. The Leptomitales

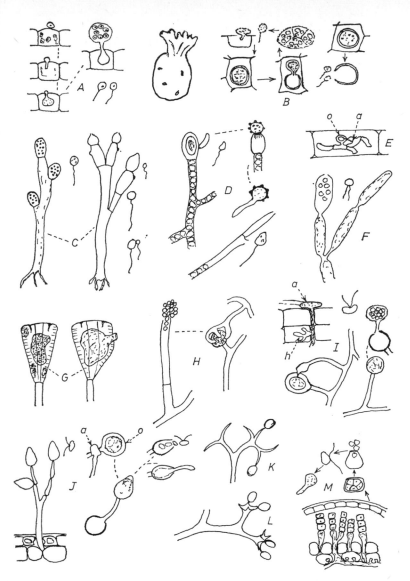

Figure 4.2. Phycomycetous fungi. A, Olpidium. *Infection of cells and formation of sporangium; B,* Synchytrium. *On left a potato with outgrowth caused by the fungal infection and stages of infection and formation of swarmers. On far right resting spore in a cell and its germination; C,* Allomyces, *on left sporophytic plant with sporangia and on right gametophyte; D,* Monoblepharis. *Plant with oogonium and antheridium on left and oospore and its germination on right. Below, zoosporangia and zoospore; E,* Lagenidium *in algal cell. Oogonium (o) with antheridium (a) penetrating the wall; F,* Leptomitus; *G,* Ectrogella *in the diatom* Licmophora—*on right with sporangium; H,* Aphanomyces—*spores encysting at mouth of sporangium and oogonium surrounded by branching antheridium; I,* Pythium. *Appressorium (a) and hyphae between host cells into which a haustorium (h) is penetrating. Also branch with oogonium and antheridium, formation of sporangium and release of spores into a vesicle; J,* Phytophthora. *Sporangiophore emerging from a stoma. Oogonium (o) with an amphigynous antheridium (a). Formation of sporangium from the oospore and germination by means of germ tube or zoospores; K, sporangiophore of* Peronospora; *L, sporangiophore of* Bremia; *M,* Albugo. *Below, chains of sporangia formed beneath the host epidermis, and above, germination of sporangium*

contain the common sewage fungus, *Leptomitus lacteus* (*Figure 4.2 F*) in which the hyphae are constricted into pseudosepta.

The large simple group Saprolegniales contains the common water moulds, but even here some genera are parasitic, e.g. *Ectrogella* in algae, some *Saprolegnia* species in fish and fish eggs and *Aphanomyces* in the roots of cultivated plants. The hyphae of *Saprolegnia* (*Figure 4.1 B*) are wide and rather coarse—elongate sporangia form at the tips and give rise to pear-shaped zoospores with the characteristic biflagellate form—the forward directed flagellum bears fine appendages and the rearwardly directed is smooth. These primary zoospores encyst and then form secondary zoospores which are kidney-shaped and with two unequal flagella. When the secondary zoospores encyst they give rise to a germ tube which grows into the new hyphal system. This phenomenon is known as *diplanetism*. The oogonia are produced terminally or in an intercalary position and adjacent to these the thin antheridial branches form and penetrate the oogonia, which may contain one or many oospheres. Some species are dioecious. The actual penetration tube is finer than the antheridium and may branch inside the oogonium. Meiosis occurs on germination of the oospores, which form a short tube out of which a zoosporangium emerges.

The Peronosporales are generally regarded as the most advanced group of Oomycetes but the simplest genera are little more advanced than *Saprolegnia* and indeed have been placed in a separate order by some workers. A notable feature of this group is the development of small sporangia on branched sporangiophores—these are deciduous and produce either swarmers or a germ tube. Since the sporangia may germinate in this latter manner they are sometimes considered as conidia but the distinction is somewhat artificial. *Pythium* species are either aquatic or require a humid environment—the spherical or pear-shaped sporangia are clearly differentiated from the mycelium and are characteristic in that on germination they form a thin-walled often stalked vesicle into which the sporangial cytoplasm passes prior to the formation of the biflagellate zoospores (*Figure 4.2 I*). The oosphere does not completely deplete the oogonium of cytoplasm and the remaining so-called periplasm contributes to the ornamentation of the oospore. Of even greater economic importance is *Phytophthora* (*Figure 4.2 J*)—one species (*P. infestans*) causes Potato Blight—still a serious disease in humid and warm regions. The fungus passes the winter as mycelium in tubers left in the ground. There are no immune varieties, but spraying with copper fungicides does reduce the incidence of the disease. Sporangiophores are formed from exposed fragments of potatoes or from stomata of leaves on shoots growing from such infected material. The sporangiophores are branched and somewhat constricted at the points where the pear-shaped sporangia arise (*Figure 4.2 J*). The sporangia germinate by means of a germ tube and when they fall on to a potato (or tomato) leaf the germ tube grows into the host via the stomata. The mycelium penetrates the host cells by the formation of a pad of mycelium (*appresorium*), which presses against the cell wall, and from the centre of this a small peg-like hypha penetrates into the host cell and then branches to form a *haustorium*, which absorbs nutriment from the cells. The hyphae growing in the host can soon form more sporangia and thus rapidly build up the infection. Under some conditions, e.g. low temperature and moisture, the sporangia can produce zoospores which then encyst and later germinate to penetrate the host cell wall. Sexual reproduction tends to be common only in warm regions, e.g. in Central America and S. America where uncultivated species of the potato are common. The oogonium grows through the antheridium during the development (*amphigynous*).

The most advanced genera of Oomycetes are all obligate parasites of terrestrial plants. Obligate parasites can only grow in host tissue and therefore it is only possible to study the stages of the life-history on and within the natural host. *Peronospora* (*Figure 4.2 K*), *Plasmopara* (*Figure 4.1 C*) and *Bremia* (*Figure 4.2 L*) all have branching sporangiophores which grow out through stomata, whilst *Albugo* (Syn. *Cystopus*) produces chains of sporangia budded off from clavate sporangiophores *beneath* the host epidermis which is uplifted and eventually splits to reveal the white mass of spores (hence the name 'white rust'). They form zoospores from the sporangia and these encyst and then 're-germinate' by means of a germ tube which invades the host and puts haustoria into the cells (*Figure 4.2 M*). Sexual reproduction, where recorded, is similar to that described for the group as a whole with the oospore releasing biflagellate swarmers on germination.

Zygomycetes

This is one of the most clearly defined groups within the lower plants. No flagellate cells have ever been found in the class (hence the designation Aplanatae, which is sometimes used); the spores germinate directly into a germ tube and are formed either in a large spherical sporangium or in various reduced few-spored 'sporangioles' or even singly (conidial state). Sexual reproduction is by the fusion of multinucleate masses formed in side branches, which grow together, fuse and form a zygospore. Species of Zygomycetes are easily trapped on moist foods or on exposed Petri dishes and are readily recognizable by the large black 'pin head' sporangia standing up from the surface and often inclined towards the light. The order Mucorales forms the largest group and although most are saprophytic, a few are weak parasites and even cause human mycoses. Species of this order are also important organisms in fermentation processes, since different species can be used to synthesize alcohol, and fumaric, citric, succinic, oxalic and lactic acids.

The hyphae of most Mucorales are rather coarse and fast-growing and in some species produce anchoring rhizoidal branches and aerial 'stolons'. The sporangia form on upright branches which swell at the tip and subsequently a basal wall forms, cutting off the sporangium. The hyphal region bulges into the sporangium forming the columella (*Figure 4.1 D*). The aplanospores are released by the bursting of the wall in most species, but in the more specialized *Pilobolus* (*Figure 4.3 C*) the apex of the sporangiophore swells greatly and perched on top of this is the actual sporangium, the upper half of which is black and cutinized; the sporangium is shot off when the sub-sporangial swelling bursts and ejects its contents.

In the Mucorales there is a tendency for branching of the sporangiophore and reduction in the number of spores in the smaller sporangia (sporangioles) formed at the apices of the branches. In some genera, e.g. *Cunninghamella* (*Figure 4.3 E*), this tendency has proceeded so far that each sporangiole contains a single spore—it is in fact a conidium. In the interesting genus *Thamnidium* the large globose *Mucor* type of sporangium is formed but branches arise lower down the sporangiophore and themselves branch and form new spored sporangioles (*Figure 4.3 D*).

Some genera are homothallic—that is the spores produced in the sporangia are all of one type and the mycelium from one spore is capable of forming the cross connexions which develop into gametangia and ultimately zygotes. Such a species is *Rhizopus sexualis* and if mycelium from a spore of this species is allowed to spread over a Petri dish then the black zygospores will be found randomly distributed over the whole plate. Other species, however, produce spores which although apparently alike, form mycelia of two physiologically different forms, and only when these two types (strains) come together do the gametangia form—this is termed heterothallism and can be shown quite strikingly if the two strains of, e.g. *Mucor hiemalis*, are seeded on opposite sides of a Petri dish since only along the line where the hyphae meet are zygospores formed. Formation of copulating branches first results in swelling of the hyphal tips to form progametangia (*Figure 4.3 A*). These then

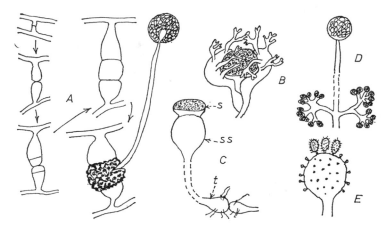

Figure 4.3. Mucorales. A, formation and germination of the zygospore of Mucor; *B, zygospore of* Phycomyces *with branched appendages growing from the suspensors; C, the sporangium (s) of* Pilobolus *sitting on the sub-sporangial swelling (ss) and growing from the 'trophocyst' (t); D,* Thamnidium, *apical sporangium and lateral sporangioles; E,* Cunninghamella, *sporangia in the form of conidia on short stalks on the swollen conidiophore*

form terminal gametangia with a large number of nuclei in each and cut off from the remains of the progametangia which now form the so-called suspensors. The wall between the gametangia now breaks down and the nuclei fuse in pairs, indiscriminately in the case of the homothallic forms and in pairs one from each strain in the heterothallic forms. This multiple zygote then lays down a thick sculptured wall to form the zygospore. On germination of the zygospore a hypha grows out through a split and forms a terminal sporangium. There are many minor variations of the above theme and some are readily visible, e.g. the development of hyphal branches growing from the suspensors and 'protecting' the zygospores in *Phycomyces* (*Figure 4.3 B*). This can be carried to a stage where a group of zygospores are enclosed in a hyphal sheath.

There are two other orders of the Zygomycetes—the Entomophthorales, growing mainly on dead insects, and the Zoopagales, which infect various animal classes. The Entomophthorales are characterized by a tendency for the hyphae to form septa and break into short hyphal bodies between which copulation occurs. These hyphal bodies also produce short clavate conidiophores forming single apical conidia.

Classification

All the fungal groups in this chapter were originally included in a single class Phycomycetes but this concept is now only valuable in distinguishing these relatively simple fungi from the higher groups. It has long been obvious that there was no overriding feature of the reproductive processes to characterize the group, such as can be easily recognized for the two groups of higher fungi, hence the splitting of the series into five classes.

Chytridiomycetes

These are fungi with *posteriorly* uniflagellate motile cells.

Chytridiales. Typical mycelium absent (*Chytridium, Olpidium, Synchytrium*)

Blastocladiales. Both gametes motile (*Allomyces*)

Monoblepharidales. Female gamete non-motile (*Monoblepharis*)

Plasmodiophoromycetes

These are parasitic, plasmodial, with unequally biflagellate swarmers.

Plasmodiophorales (*Plasmodiophora*)

Oomycetes

These fungi have non-motile egg cells.

Saprolegniales. Hyphae unconstricted and zoospores formed within a sporangium (*Saprolegnia, Aphanomyces, Ectrogella*)

Leptomitales. Hyphae constricted (*Leptomitus*)

Lagenidiales. Thallus completely converted into zoosporangia during asexual reproduction (*Lagenidium*)

Peronosporales. Sporangia cut off from thallus and often forming a vesicle into which the spores flow (*Peronospora, Pythium, Phytophthora, Bremia, Albugo*)

Zygomycetes

Fungi in which a zygospore arises from the fusion of two gametangia.

Mucorales. Sporangia produce one or many aplanospores or conidia (*Cunninghamella, Mucor, Pilobolus, Thamnidium, Rhizopus, Phycomyces*)

Entomophthorales. Conidia only formed.

Practical Study

1. Hang fruits (e.g. tomato, apple, etc.) or seeds in any garden pond or local pond as bait for aquatic forms of the Saprolegniales, etc.

2. Chytrids are common in some waters on algae and dead skins of insects, etc., but they are relatively inconspicuous. A sample of plankton often reveals chytrids on some of the algae. Unfortunately the populations rapidly assume epidemic proportions and are therefore only present over a short period of time.

3. Water and decaying leaves, etc., from ponds may be put into Petri dishes and these 'seeded' with seeds, etc., on which the aquatic forms will often grow.

4. Open a few dishes containing agar (or table-jelly if agar is not available) and the probability is that spores of the Mucorales will fall on the dishes and grow. (N.B. So will other fungi of the higher groups.)

5. Dung or decaying food brought into the laboratory and put under a bell-jar often produces a good crop of fungi.

6. If sporangia of the Mucorales form on any of the plates, try and pick these off and break open on to a fresh plate to obtain a pure culture.

7. Study the germination of spores on agar plates or on films of agar on slides. Design experiments to investigate the effect of environmental features on spore germination.

8. Keep some infected plates at different temperatures and measure the diameter of the colonies daily and plot a graph of their growth. These can be measured from the underside of the dish and the lids need not be removed.

9. Observe living hyphae under the high power of the microscope and look for cytoplasmic movement and variation from the tip backwards.

10. Collect any plant material showing fungal hyphae on the leaves and look for members of the Peronosporales. Try to germinate the spores if these are found.

Fungi are so widely distributed that your problems are most likely to involve separation and recognition of the groups rather than failure to find fungi.

Review Questions

1. What are the characteristic features of 'phycomycetous' fungi?

Why has it been necessary to subdivide this group and what are the major characteristics used in this subdivision?

2. Can you see any similarities between these groups and the algae? After all, 'phycomycetes' means algal fungi. Is there any particular algal group from which they are more likely to have arisen?

3. Review the methods of asexual reproduction in these fungi.

4. Review the methods of sexual reproduction in these fungi. Is there any correlation between the development of oogamy and other features of morphology and distribution?

5. What do we mean by 'saprophytism,' 'facultative' and 'obligate' parasitism? Give examples of these modes of life.

6. Are there any obvious advantages or disadvantages of conidia over planospores?

7. Trace the modifications which appear to have occurred in the Peronosporales in the change from an aquatic to a terrestrial existence.

8. Discuss the economic importance of these lower fungi.

BIBLIOGRAPHY

ALEXOPOULOS, C. J., *Introductory Mycology* (2nd edn) Wiley, New York, 1962

BESSEY, E. A., *Morphology and Taxonomy of Fungi*, The Blakiston Co., Philadelphia, 1950

HAWKER, L. E., *Fungi. An Introduction*, Hutchinson, London, 1966

HAWKER, L. E., *et al. An Introduction to the Biology of Micro-Organisms*, Edward Arnold, London, 1960

INGOLD, C. T., *The Biology of Fungi*, Hutchinson Educational Ltd., London, 1961

LARGE, E. C., *The Advance of the Fungi*, Henry Holt, New York, 1940

SMITH, G. M., *Cryptogamic Botany*, Vol. I, McGraw-Hill, New York, 1938

5

THE FUNGI—GROUPS CHARACTERIZED BY THE FORMATION OF ASCI

THIS very large group of fungi (Ascomycetes) causes considerable damage to vegetation and man-made goods but is less obvious to casual observation since fewer striking fruiting structures are formed compared with the next group—Basidiomycetes. However, a few do form fruiting bodies superficially similar to the latter group, e.g. the morels (*Morchella* spp.)—but more commonly they are recognizable by the black, often hard, structures growing on leaves (e.g. the common tar spot, *Rhytisma acerinum* which most students will have seen on Sycamore or Maple leaves) or on decomposing stems and twigs, e.g. the black structures as large as or larger and as hard as golf balls, of genera such as *Daldinia*. Almost any small patch of vegetation will yield examples of this group whilst an exposed agar plate will almost invariably grow examples of the conidial stage of *Aspergillus* or *Penicillium*. Estimates of 1700 genera have been made for this group, which makes it by far the largest of lower plants and along with the red algae one of the most complex groups.

As with the red algae, a feature of their sexual reproduction forms the unifying characteristic of the group and clearly distinguishes it from any other. This structure is a sporangium known as the ascus, which forms a definite number of ascospores (usually eight) by meiotic division followed by one mitotic division. No motile flagellated cell is known in the group, which in general has septate hyphae with chitinous walls. Conidia germinating with a germ tube are frequent and tend to be formed on characteristic branched-conidiophores. Both the conidiophores and the asci may be grouped, and particularly around the latter, a complex fruiting body can form.

As in the lower plant groups there has existed the problem of fitting the asexual/conidial producing stage (imperfect stage) to the sexual/ascospore stage (perfect stage) and there are still many problems here—a large group of fungi are still known in the imperfect stage, but gradually the number is being reduced as they are linked with the ascus producing part of the life history (a much smaller number finally turn out to be Basidiomycetes). These fungi, in which only the imperfect stage is known, and in which the hyphae are septate, are often artificially classed together as the Fungi Imperfect or the Deuteromycetes. Less common are the Ascomycetes in which the imperfect stage is unknown.

In no other group is there such a proliferation of asexual spore forms and spore-bearing structures. Spores may be unicellular or septate, round, oval, sickle- or needle-shaped, formed on relatively undifferentiated hyphae, on flask-like phialides, globose conidiophores, etc. (*Figures 4.1 F, 5.1* and *5.2*). The fungal hyphae may aggregate to form plate-like masses of hyphae often below the epidermis of the host (acervulus) or a flask-shaped fruiting body (pycnidium, *Figure 5.2 A*) inside which the spores are budded off, or the hyphae may aggregate to form a horn-like structure bearing a terminal mass of spores—a coremium.

The essence of sexual reproduction is the bringing together of two compatible nuclei and the Ascomycetes do this in a variety of ways though generally without any strikingly obvious male gametangial formation. In some species the 'male' and 'female' hyphal branches touch or coil around one another and a breakdown of the walls occurs at some point to produce a fusion cell (*Figure 5.1 A, F*). In others the antheridium is a simple hyphal branch and the female branch or ascogonium is a cell with a trichogyne into which the male nucleus migrates after contact between the two. In yet other forms, male cells (spermatia) are formed rather as in red algae and carried by wind, water or insects to the ascogonium—sometimes cells of this nature can germinate and perpetuate the vegetative phase of the life cycle, they are then termed microconidia (e.g. *Figure 5.2 F*). In some genera there is merely fusion between vegetative hyphae and then transport of the nuclei to the ascogonium. Some Ascomycetes are homothallic whilst others are heterothallic due to segregation of a pair of genes at meiosis (e.g. *Neurospora*).

Often the nuclei from the two parents come to lie adjacent but do not fuse for some time (a dikaryon)—they may in fact undergo simultaneous division so that the 'dikaryon' is reproduced. Ultimately the dikaryon of the ascogonium moves out into one, or after division into several, 'ascogenous hyphae' which grow out from the ascogonium. At the tip of this special hypha, 'crozier' formation occurs in which the tip curls over and the dikaryon divides and two compatible nuclei remain in the angle of the crozier; one is cut off in the curved apical cell and the other is cut off on the other side of the cell containing the dikaryon (*Figure 5.2 J*). It is in this binucleate cell (sometimes called the 'crook cell') that karyogamy occurs and this zygotic nucleus is the only diploid phase in the cycle. From this the ascus elongates and after meiosis the spores form around the nuclei (*Figure 5.2 J*), often as a linear series of 8, but in some there may be more or less, depending on further mitotic divisions or abortions. The isolated antheridial or ascogonial nuclei isolated on either side of the ascus mother cell can be reunited by a fusion between these two cells and these can proceed to form yet another crozier and so on to initiate a succession of asci. Characteristics of the ascus and ascospores are important in the classification of species

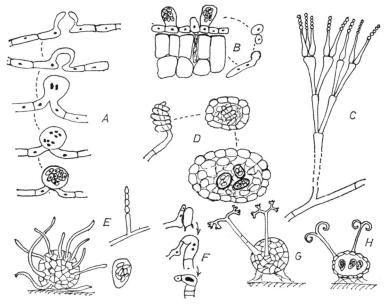

Figure 5.1. Simple ascomycetous fungi. A, Eremascus. *Stages in the formation of an ascus; B,* Taphrina *growing on the surface of the host and forming asci; C, conidiophore of* Penicillium; *D, development of asci in cleistothecium—on the left the copulating branches; E,* Sphaerotheca—*cleistothecium, and on right a conidiophore, and an ascus containing eight asci; F, formation of ascus mother cell in the Ascohymeniales; G, cleistothecium of* Podosphaera; *H, cleistothecium of* Uncinula *containing several asci*

and genera. Size, shape, colour and number of ascospores are valuable characteristics as is the nature of the ascus wall. In the unitunicate series the ascus wall is a single layer whilst in the bitunicate series the outer wall is rigid; this splits at the apex and the inner extensible wall tends to expand through this (*Figure 5.2 G*). Clusters of asci in a layer together with any interspersed sterile paraphyses constitute a hymenium.

A few genera form their asci directly on the mycelium and no fruiting structure is formed, but the majority have a distinct hymenial region surrounded by sterile hyphae (an ascocarp), forming either a closed structure (a cleistothecium, *Figure 5.1 D, E, G, H*) or a similar structure, but provided with a pore for the escape of the ascospores (perithecium, *Figure 4.1 I*), or an open cup-shaped structure (apothecium, *Figures 4.1 G, 5.2 E*). Yet others bear the asci in cavities within a stroma, i.e. in the compacted hyphal aggregate (ascostroma, *Figure 5.2 H, I*) which forms part of the fungal growth. These varied ascocarps may commence growth after plasmogamy has occurred, or they may be initiated before the sexual organs, which then at a later date become differentiated within the developing ascocarp.

Although many aspects of the classification of Ascomycetes are still being debated there is general agreement that three major series (sub-classes) are involved; Hemiascomycetidae—asci are naked and no ascogenous hyphae are formed; Euascomycetidae—have unitunicate asci in ascocarps, but some are bitunicate and then the fruit body is an apothecium; Loculoascomycetidae—bitunicate asci in ascostromata.

Hemiascomycetidae (Protoascomycetidae)

The most important fungi in this sub-class are the yeasts, which are very abundant in nature, particularly on fruits, in soil and in water. One yeast used in commercial processes is *Saccharomyces cerevisiae*, which is grown specially for baking and brewing. It is a single-celled fungus which grows by budding (*Figure 4.1 E*), its only means of asexual reproduction. Sexual reproduction involves the fusion of two cells. The nuclei fuse and this diploid cell can bud in a similar manner to the haploid cells. At some stage these diploid cells become converted into asci with the production of *four* ascospores. This yeast is heterothallic, but not all yeasts are. Some yeasts divide in a normal manner by formation of cross walls. There are a large number of yeasts and in fact the monographs on this group alone are much larger than this book. They are classified on shape, method of growth, form and colour of colonies, number and shape of ascospores and many biochemical characteristics.

The important property of yeast is its ability to absorb sugars and metabolize them with the production of alcohol and carbon dioxide. This is achieved in the absence of oxygen and is in fact an example of anaerobic respiration or fermentation.

Another hemiascomycete is *Eremascus*, which illustrates in a very simple manner the life history of a filamentous form in which two gametangial branches fuse, the fusion cell undergoes meiosis and becomes the ascus (*Figure 5.1 A*).

Plant parasites are also included within this group—*Taphrina deformans* causes peach leaf curl from growth of the mycelia amongst the surface cells of the leaves—it is not a serious disease and can be controlled by spraying with copper fungicides. The plant is unusual in that no sexual cells are formed. All the cells of the mycelium are binucleate and ascus formation occurs when one of these enlarges and the two nuclei fuse. Ascospores form and after release they behave somewhat like a yeast and bud off cells (conidia or blastospores). When these germinate the nucleus divides and then conjugate division of the daughter nuclei continues to maintain a binucleate condition in each cell (*Figure 5.1 B*).

Euascomycetidae

This very large group is subdivided into three series based on the morphology of the fruiting body; in the Plectomycetes the asci are scattered in the ascocarp, in the Pyrenomycetes the ascocarp is a perithecium whilst in the Discomycetes it is an apothecium or modification of this.

The best known Plectomycetes are *Aspergillus* and *Penicillium*, which are mainly known as form genera, in that it is the conidial stage which has been found and only in a few instances has this been linked with the ascospore producing stage. *Aspergillus* is very easy to cultivate on plates of nutrient agar and the colonies often have a green, bluish or black colour. It is responsible for several respiratory diseases (aspergilloses) but is also used in the manufacture of organic acids and in the production of the Japanese alcoholic drink 'Sake'. The conidiophores form as branches from a thickened 'foot cell' and swell at the apex, from which numerous flask-like sterigmata arise cutting off conidia in chains, actually from inside the tube-like tip of the sterigmata (*Figure 4.1 F*). In sexual reproduction (which may have been lost in many species) the ascocarps form as loose interwoven masses of hyphae (cleistothecia). *Penicillium* is equally abundant and occurs in nature, especially on citrus fruits. Like *Aspergillus* it is important commercially in the production of organic acids, but also in cheese making, e.g. in Danish Blue, Gorgonzola and Roquefort whilst perhaps most important of all *P. notatum* and *P. chrysogenum* produce the valuable antibiotic, penicillin. The generic name refers to the little brush-like structures which form the conidiophores (*Figure 5.1 C*). The conidia are formed as in *Aspergillus* and it is the coloration of these which gives rise to the characteristic colony tints.

The Ascohymeniales—a small sub-group of the Plectomycetes—contain an important group of obligate parasites, the powdery

77

mildews (Erisiphales). Some occur on a wide variety of hosts whilst some are specific to a single host plant. They vary in their economic importance—some causing little damage to the host and others capable of destroying whole crops, e.g. *Uncinula* on grapes. In a few species, hyphae grow into the intercellular spaces, but more commonly the mycelium grows over the leaf surface and haustoria penetrate only the epidermal cells. The 'powdery' nature of these fungi is due to the chains of conidia budding off from simple hypha-like conidiophores on the leaf surface (*Figure 5.1 E*). Ascogonia and antheridia form amongst the hyphae and the developing asci (one in *Sphaerotheca* and *Podosphaera* and many in the other genera) become enclosed in a cleistocarp of several layers of pseudoparenchyma provided with long appendages which branch in different ways in the different genera (*Figure 5.1 E, G, H*). The asci are usually club-shaped and germinate to give the mycelial stage. The cleistocarp is often the overwintering organ though in some regions sexual stages are rare and the fungus persists through the conidial stage. Control of powdery mildews is possible through dusting with sulphur-containing compounds.

The most studied genus of the Pyrenomycetes is *Neurospora*, since this organism has proved highly suitable for genetic and biochemical studies. The mycelium is pigmented and forms pink conidia and small black perithecia. There are no antheridia and the ascogonium forms long branched trichogynes which receive the male nuclei in the form of conidia or microconidia. The genus is heterothallic and the complexity of the life history is shown in *Figure 5.2 F*. *Xylaria* and *Daldinia* are common genera, producing macroscopic fruiting bodies; in the former the hyphae are aggregated into black antler-shaped stromata with white tips and in *Daldinia* the stromata are black hemispherical cushions—both grow on wood and can be serious parasites. The perithecia are embedded in the stroma (*Figure 4.1 I*). Another genus which most students will have seen is *Nectria*; this forms pink or red hemispherical lumps breaking through the bark of twigs. The pink structures are the 'sporodochia', bearing numerous conidiophores and oval conidia. The deeper red structures are the same stromata which later in the season begin to produce perithecia (*Figure 5.2 D*). Another not uncommon genus (*Claviceps*) causes 'ergot' of rye—the fungus infects the flowers and after invasion of the ovary converts this into a mass of mycelium on which conidiophores are produced, later the hyphal mass hardens and is known as a sclerotium; it resembles the rye grain in shape (*Figure 5.2 C*). This sclerotium produces small outgrowths which swell at the tips and in which the perithecia are embedded. The sclerotia (ergots) contain poisonous alkaloids and in the past have been left in the grain after milling, resulting in poisoning.

The Discomycetes include the easily recognizable cup fungi such as the orange or brown coloured *Peziza* (*Figure 4.1 G*) which form large fleshy apothecia. Others have convoluted apothecia, e.g. *Morchella* (*Figure 4.1 H*) and yet others have the ascocarps closed over, e.g. the hypogean Tuberales (truffles). Apart from the separation into the above ground (epigean) and subterranean (hypogean) groups, the mode of dehiscence of the ascus is utilized in classification—some merely perforate at the tip (inoperculate series) whilst others have a distinct operculum with a hinged lid-like structure (operculate series). Many are saprophytic but others are the cause of serious plant diseases. In *Rhytisma* the apothecia develop in the 'tar spots' on sycamore or maple leaves (*Figure 5.2 A*). They are at first closed over but as the hymenium matures, splits appear in the black stroma to reveal the layer of asci, containing filamentous ascospores. Prior to ascus formation small pits form in the young stroma and inside these spermatia are produced—these have not been observed to infect leaves or act as male cells, in fact some authors term them conidia. Brown rot of stone and pome fruits is caused by *Sclerotinia* (*Monilinia*) *fructicola* (*Figure 5.2 E*). The fungus spreads rapidly by means of oval conidia budded off in chains (*Monilinia* stage). Later in the season the hyphae, which have spread throughout the fruits, cause these to shrivel and mummify—they may often be found attached to the trees during winter. However, those which fall off become buried and in later years long stalked apothecia grow from these mummified fruits. Spermatia or microconidia are formed but they have not been seen to function.

Loculoascomycetidae

This final group has bitunicate asci within locules in stromatic masses rather than forming in specially developed structures. In *Myriangium*, which parasitizes insects, single asci form in the locules, but in genera such as *Mycosphaerella* and *Venturia* (*Figure 5.2 H, I*) many asci grow in each locule. These latter genera are important plant parasites, the former attacking the leaves of many plants and the latter causing apple and pear scab. Like so many other diseases it spreads rapidly by the production of conidia. Control is achieved by repeated spraying with mercury-containing fungicides.

Classification

This is yet another group which emphasizes the importance which

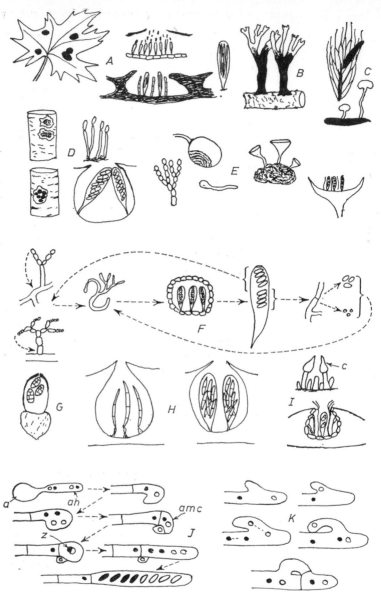

Figure 5.2. Ascomycetes and the formation of asci and clamp connexions in the basidiomycetes. A, Rhytisma—*'tar spot' on leaf and on right sections of these showing formation of spermogonia in the early stage, and later of apothecia with asci containing filiform ascospores; B, fruiting body of* Xylaria *growing on a twig; C,* Claviceps—*above, the sclerotium (ergot) in a spike of rye and below, the formation of stalked apothecia on the ergot; D,* Nectria. *Formation of conidial patches breaking through bark and below, the same patches with*

is attached to sexual reproductive structures in establishing a classificatory system. The structures containing the asci, i.e. the ascocarps, the method of formation and structure of the ascus are of prime importance.

Three sub-classes are immediately obvious. Hemiascomycetidae —with naked asci and no ascogenous hyphae; Euascomycetidae— with unitunicate asci in ascocarps or with bitunicate asci but then enclosed within an apothecium; Loculoascomycetidae—bitunicate asci in ascostromata.

Hemiascomycetidae
    Yeast and leaf curl fungi.
    Endomycetales (*Eremascus, Saccharomyces*)
    Taphrinales (*Taphrina*)

Euascomycetidae
    (*a*) Plectomycete series
        Eurotiales (*Aspergillus, Penicillium*)
    (*b*) Pyrenomycete series
        Ascohymeniales (*Erysiphe, Sphaerotheca, Podosphaera, Uncinula*)
        Sphacriales (*Neurospora, Xylaria, Daldinia, Nectria, Claviceps*)
    (*c*) Discomycete series
        Inoperculate asci: Helotiales (*Rhytisma, Monilinia, Sclerotinia*)
        Operculate asci: Pezizales (*Peziza, Morchella*)

Loculoascomycetidae
    Myriangiales (*Myriangium*)
    Dothideales (*Mycosphaerella*)
    Pleosporales (*Venturia*)

---

perithecia. On right the conidia and asci with bicellular ascospores; E, Sclerotinia. A fruit with the concentric growth of the fungus and below, the conidia. On the right a mummified fruit bearing apothecia and a section of one of these; F, the life cycle of Neurospora. On the left, formation of conidia and below, of microconidia. In the centre the branching female system, asci in a perithecium and an ascus with four ascospores of each strain. These germinate to give mycelium producing conidia and microconidia of the two strain types. Formation of asci shown only from the strain on the left—similar sequence from the other strain; G, Myriangium, ascus of the bitunicate type and multicellular ascospores; H, Mycosphaerella —pycnidia with multicellular conidia on left and ascocarp on right; I, Venturia—above, formation of conidia (c) and ascocarp below; J, sequence of divisions to form ascus mother cell and ascus with eight ascospores. Ascogonium (a) giving rise to the ascogenous hypha (ah). Ascus mother cell, (amc). Fusion to form a zygote (z) in the ascus followed by divisions to form ascospores; K, formation of clamp connexions in a basidiomycete yielding an apical cell with nuclei from the two parent strains which will fuse to form the basidial nucleus

Practical Study

1. Obtain some bakers yeast and study the structure of the yeast cell. Grow in sugar solution and observe budding (a little added nitrogen may help growth). Scrape the surface of mature fruits and plate out on agar—this is often a good source of yeast cells. They may also occur on plates you have seeded from aquatic and other sources.

2. If you set up plates for *Mucor*, etc., they will almost certainly grow either or both *Aspergillus* and *Penicillium*. Study the structure of the conidiophores. Attempt to make pure cultures from the spores. Note the different morphology and coloration of the colonies.

3. Look for white powdery growths on leaves and take back to the laboratory. Use a lens or dissecting microscope and look for cleistothecia. (N.B. The white growths may not necessarily belong to species of the Ascohymeniales.) If cleistothecia are found, note the form of the appendages and squash to see the asci. Powdery mildews are not uncommon—they have been reported on hundreds of angiosperm species.

4. Collect any black ascocarps growing on live or dead twigs and also black stroma on leaves and stems, e.g. *Rhytisma,* which most students will be able to find. Section these wherever possible and look for the asci.

5. Look for apothecia—particularly in moist woodland. *Peziza* and related forms are quite common. Some of these forms are also common on dung. Fruit trees often yield decayed fruits and the asexual and apothecial stages of the fruit rotting fungi can be found.

Review Questions

1. Review the major characteristics of the Ascomycetes. What features have they in common with the 'phycomycete' series?

2. Write a short account of sexual reproduction in the Ascomycetes. What is the particular significance of the formation of the 'crook cell'.

3. Review the range of asexual spore formation in this group. Why is it that they are so common on opened agar plates, exposed food, etc.?

4. Few plant groups form such tough protective layers around the sporing structures. What may be the significance of these?

5. How important are the Ascomycetes to man? Distinguish their harmful and beneficial aspects.

BIBLIOGRAPHY

ALEXOPOULOS, C. J., *Introductory Mycology* (2nd edn), Wiley, New York, 1962

GÄUMANN, E. A. and DODGE, C. W., *Comparative Morphology of Fungi*, McGraw-Hill, New York, 1928

HAWKER, L. E., *Fungi. An Introduction*, Hutchinson, London, 1966

INGOLD, C. T., *Dispersal in Fungi*, Clarendon Press, Oxford, 1953

6

THE FUNGI—GROUPS CHARACTERIZED BY THE FORMATION OF BASIDIA

THIS group includes one of the most obviously economically important lower plants—the cultivated mushroom, and also some of the most destructive lower plants—the rusts, smuts, dry rot and many other timber rotting fungi. Basidiomycetes form a well circumscribed group in which meiosis is initiated in a swollen cell, the basidium (or in a septate basidium), and usually only four spores result and these are formed within short horns (sterigmata) on which they eventually become balanced prior to discharge. Unlike the Ascomycetes, where the dikaryophase is initiated in the ascogonium, this phase in the Basidiomycetes starts soon after germination of the basidiospores by fusion between compatible hyphae. The mycelial cells then all contain pairs of nuclei which do not fuse until a basidium is formed. To ensure that at cell division each daughter cell receives one nucleus of each parental type, a system of so-called *clamp connexions* has evolved (*Figure 5.2 K*). These operate in a manner comparable to the hooks of the ascogenous hyphae in the Ascomycetes and some authorities consider this a feature suggesting a fairly close evolutionary relationship. The electron microscope has revealed characteristic pores in the cross walls of the basidiomycetous hyphae—these (*doliopores*) are flared at the centre and are associated with collections of endoplasmic reticulum on either side known as parenthosomes. The fruit bodies or basidiocarps are very varied—the commonest known forms are the mushrooms, bracket fungi on trees and the puff-balls (*Figure 6.2*). The basidia are clustered into tissues—hymenia—usually enclosed at first and then exposed as the surrounding tissues tear, e.g. in most mushrooms (*Figure 6.2 A*), but occasionally the basidia are formed on relatively unorganized mycelial growths. In a large group (Gasteromycetes) the hymenial surface remains enclosed until the spores have been released into cavities within the fruit body. Sterile cells occur amongst the basidia in the hymenium (*Figure 6.2 C*) and some grow quite large and swollen (*cystidia*) but there is not the distinct formation of sterile paraphyses as in the Ascomycetes. The spores themselves are enclosed in a wall and also in the wall of the sterigmata on which they were formed. They are explosively ejected, often carrying a spot of water which forms at the tip of the sterigmata. Spore colour is a valuable aid to identification and is easily detected by placing a mature 'mushroom' head on a piece of white paper and leaving overnight to produce a 'spore print'. Asexual reproduction, although less obvious in the Basidiomycetes, is in fact widespread by budding, mycelial fragmentation, production of conidia, oidia or chlamydospores.

Much remains to be achieved in the classification of this large group but the basic entities are fairly clear. The nature of the basidium forms the primary division into Heterobasidiomycetidae in which the basidium is septate or deeply divided (or is a thick-walled teleutospore giving rise to a short tube on which the basidiospores are borne) and the Homobasidiomycetidae in which the basidium is a simple clavate structure. The latter sub-class is divided into the Hymenomycete series, which includes the Polyporales and Agaricales, i.e. forms in which the hymenium is exposed, and the Gasteromycetes, which have closed fruit bodies until the spores have been released.

Heterobasidiomycetidae

Two important groups of plant parasites—'smuts and rusts'—form a major part of this section. The 'smuts' form masses of black 'brand spores' or teleutospores in the ovaries of Gramineae (*Figure 6.1 A*), in the anthers (particularly in plants of the Caryophyllaceae) or in streak-like sori on the leaves. They are all in the Ustilaginales and although they are inter-cellular parasites they are not obligate parasites since they can be cultivated on agar. Another peculiarity of this group is the tendency for the parasitic mycelium to concentrate in the meristematic zones of the plant without causing too much damage to vegetative growth. The 'smut' spore germinates to form a short septate promycelium which is in fact a septate basidium producing sickle-shaped basidiospores (*Tilletia*) each containing haploid nuclei; these spores then fuse in pairs (*Figure 6.1 B*) and give rise to dikaryotic secondary spores. In *Ustilago* the walls between the cells of the promycelium break down to produce dikaryotic cells, or sporidia are formed which fuse to give rise to the dikaryotic phase.

The rusts (Uredinales) are much more complex and are mostly obligate parasites producing coloured (often red) sori which burst through the leaf or stem tissue of the host. There are many genera causing considerable damage to crops ranging from cereals, through timber trees to many cultivated herbs and shrubs. Recently a few species have been grown in artificial media. Almost all have complex life-cycles with up to five stages in the life history and also two alternate host plants—a state known as *heteroecism*. If, however, they

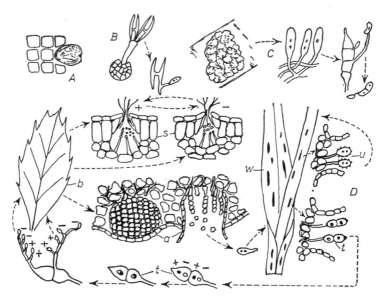

Figure 6.1. Heterobasidiomycetidae. A, swollen fruit of maize infected by Ustilago; *B, brand spore of* Tilletia *giving rise to promycelium and fusing sporidia. On right, sporidia forming conidium; C,* Auricularia *on twig and formation of septate basidia. Germination of these to form a spore and its germination to form a conidium; D, the life cycle of* Puccinia graminis. *Stages on* Berberis (*b*) *on left and on wheat* (*w*) *on right. Spermogonia* (*s*), *aecidia* (*a*), *uredospores* (*u*), *teleutospores* (*t*) *and segregation of nuclei into* + *and* − *strains*

complete all stages of development on a single host they are termed *autoecious*. The most infamous of all the rusts is *Puccinia graminis*, causing 'black stem rust' of wheat and having species of *Berberis* as alternate host. The resistant over-wintering stage in the life history is the two-celled teleutospore in which nuclear fusion occurs between the pair of nuclei of + and − strains in each cell (*Figure 6.1 D*). Germination in the spring results in a germ tube from each cell and meiotic division of the nucleus. Cross walls form and each segment gives rise to a sterigma on which a basidiospore forms (2 + and 2 −). These infect *Berberis* plants and the monokaryotic mycelium penetrates between the host cells whilst inserting haustoria into the cells. With quite remarkable speed this mycelium aggregates to form flask-shaped spermogonia (pycnidia) amongst the superficial cells on the *upper* surface of the leaf. Thin spermatiophores radiate into the spermogonium and out through the ostiole cutting off small unicellular spermatia. Other receptive hyphae also develop and protrude through the ostiole to receive spermatia of the opposite strain—insects transfer spermatia as they move from one spermogonium to another, feeding on the sugary exudate. Fusion between a spermatium and a receptive hypha results in the re-establishment of the dikaryophase. Meanwhile, amongst the tissues of the *lower* surface of the leaf the hyphae aggregate to form aecidial initials which when supplied with dikaryotic nuclei continue development to form the aecidia (aecia), which consist of rows of binucleate aecidiospores separated by sterile 'disjunctor' cells. During development the aecidiospores are completely surrounded by a sterile wall ('peridium') and as development continues the blister bursts through the epidermal cells and the peridium tears to reveal the aecidiospores. These spores are unable to reinfect *Berberis* but when they germinate on the surface of a cereal leaf the germ tube grows through the stomatal opening. From the mycelium, which then proliferates amongst the superficial cells, stalked uredospores are formed which on release act as accessory reproductive cells, transferring the infection to other cereal plants. They arc binucleate and have two lateral germ pores. In these same sori black spores begin to appear in later summer—these are the two-celled teleutospores which over-winter and only infect the alternate host *Berberis*. Obviously elimination of the alternate host will assist the control of the disease, but unfortunately the uredospores can be carried great distances in air currents. Crop spraying from aircraft is used on a large scale in extensive wheat growing areas, whilst many resistant varieties have been produced by intensive breeding programmes—unfortunately the parasite itself can adapt, so constant vigilance is required. By no means do all species of *Puccinia* nor all genera in the Uredinales have all the phases in the life history just described for *P. graminis*—some dispense with the aecidial stage and some with the uredospores also.

Finally, amongst the heterobasidiomycetidae there is an order (Tremellales) in which the basidia are borne in a hymenium over the surface of a fruit body, e.g. the Jews Ear fungus (*Auricularia auricula*) which commonly forms jelly-like fructifications on *Sambucus* (Elder) twigs. The basidia, however, are septate (*Figure 6.1 C*).

Homobasidiomycetidae

The Hymenomycete series contain the common and easily recognizable mushrooms and toadstools, but these are only the fruit bodies of usually extensive hidden mycelial growths which permeate the soil, and are responsible for a considerable amount of the decomposition of organic remains. Many form mycelial growths (mycorrhiza) around the roots of trees and derive some organic nutriment from the tree, but in return absorb inorganic salts in an extensive weft of mycelia and convey these back to the roots, thus greatly extending the absorption area of the roots. Other genera have mycelial strands which penetrate many trees and cause consider-able losses of timber—they are often recognizable by the formation of bracket-like outgrowths from the stems, e.g. in the genus *Polyporus* (Polyporales), which has the basidia lining tubes on the under-surface of the fruit body (*Figure 6.2 K*).

Most of the mushroom-like fungi are included in the larger order Agaricales, in which the cap or pileus bears flat 'gills' radiating from the stem or stipe (*Figure 6.2*). In early development small button-like swellings appear on the underground mycelial strands and gradually swell to form short stalks and hemispherical caps. Between the cap and the stalk a chamber appears and on the upper side of this the gills form. Rapid expansion of the fruit body tears the connexion between the rim of the cap and the stalk leaving the torn tissue as an annulus around the stipe (*Figure 6.2 A, B*) and sometimes also hanging down from the rim of the pileus as the cor-tina. In the genus *Amanita*, a further layer of tissue covers the whole of the developing basidiocarp, and as expansion occurs this also tears leaving fragments on the pileus in the form of scales and a cup-like structure (volva) at the base of the stipe (*Figure 6.2 I*). Some mush-rooms contain hallucinogenic chemicals and yet others poisonous substances, and since the identification of species of 'mushrooms' is difficult they should be eaten only when they have been identified by experienced persons. Some examples are illustrated in *Figure 6.2*.

The commonest Gasteromycetes are perhaps the puff-balls (*Lycoperdon* and *Scleroderma*; *Figures 6.2 L and 4.1 K*) found on the ground or on decaying wood. The spores are formed in cavities which gradually enlarge producing basidia on their internal surfaces. At maturity the whole of the inside is full of spores and the outer layer (peridium) becomes papery and holes appear, from which the spores are 'puffed' out whenever the fruit body is disturbed. Other genera have more complex peridia which split into layers and ex-pand as in the earth star (*Geastrum*) (*Figure 6.2 M*). In the bird's nest fungi (e.g. *Crucibulum*, *Figure 6.2 N*) the fruit body is cup-shaped and the hymenium is developed within small egg-like structures (peridiola) borne on elastic mucilaginous stalks within the cups.

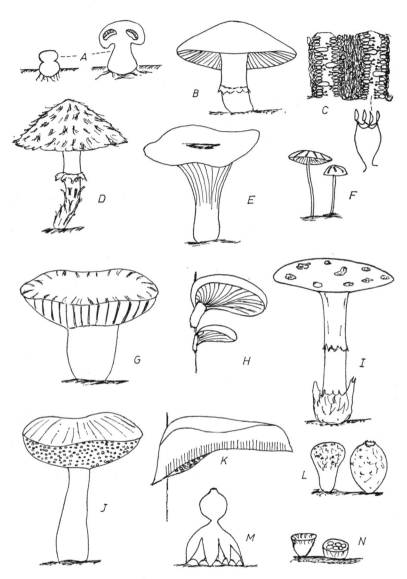

Figure 6.2. Homobasidiomycetidae. A, the development of the hymenium in a young fruit body; B, Agaricus; C, section of an hymenium and below a basidium with four basidiospores; D, Pholiota; E, Cantharellus; F, Marasmius; G, Russula; H, Pleurotus; I, Amanita; J, Boletus; K, Polyporus; L, Lycoperdon; M, Geastrum; N, Crucibulum

Classification

The septate basidial genera form a distinct sub-class—Heterobasidiomycetidae, whilst the undivided basidial genera form the second and larger sub-class—Homobasidiomycetidae.

Heterobasidiomycetidae
  Ustilaginales (*Ustilago, Tilletia*)
  Uredinales (*Puccinia*)
  Tremellales (*Auricularia*)

Homobasidiomycetidae
  Hymenomycete series. Hymenia exposed before spores are mature.
    Polyporales (*Polyporus, Cantarellus*)
    Agaricales (*Agaricus, Coprinus, Boletus, Marasmius, Pholiota, Pleurotus, Russula, Amanita*)
  Gasteromycete series. Spores mature inside the fruit body.
    Lycoperdales (*Lycoperdon, Geastrum*)
    Sclerodermatales (*Scleroderma*)
    Nidulariales (*Crucibulun*)

Practical Study

1. Look for 'smuts' or 'rusts' on Angiosperms. The anthers of some plants are converted into masses of spores and they appear deformed—these are not, however, easy to recognize until you have had them pointed out. Orange or black powdery patches or streaks on leaves and stems indicate infection by rusts. Take back to the laboratory and section.

2. Make a collection of 'mushrooms'. Note the general features of development. Section the hymenial region. Remove the stipes of a range of these and place the pileus hymenial surface down on sheets of white paper to obtain spore prints.

3. Section young stages of 'mushrooms' and 'puff-balls' to see the developing hymenia.

Review Questions

1. In what ways do the Basidiomycetes parallel the Ascomycetes?

2. Review the reproductive processes of the Basidiomycetes. What is the significance of 'clamp connexions'.

3. Write a short account of 'smuts' and 'rusts'. What features have these groups in common?

4. How does the diploid phase and the production of basidiospores in 'rusts' differ from that in other basidiomycetes?

5. What is meant by the terms 'heteroecious' and 'autoecious'? What may be the advantages or disadvantages of these states to the fungus?

6. How ubiquitous are the Basidiomycetes. The 'mushroom' stage is obvious to the eye but what effect does the growth of the mycelium have?

BIBLIOGRAPHY

ALEXOPOULOS, C. J., *Introductory Mycology* (2nd edn) Wiley, New York, 1962

7

THE LICHENS

THIS group is one of the most unusual in the plant kingdom since the 400 genera are all symbionts consisting of algal cells embedded in fungal mycelia. They are macroscopic plants, often whitish or greenish grey in colour but sometimes brightly pigmented owing to the accumulation of carotenoid pigments in the thalli. They are very slow growing and often occur in rather extreme habitats, e.g. on tree bark, rock surfaces and very abundantly on the peaty soils in Arctic and mountain regions, e.g. reindeer moss of the Arctic tundra and Spanish moss hanging from trees in warmer parts of America. Others are aquatic, mainly in fresh waters, although a small group occur on rocks in the inter-tidal zone (e.g. *Verrucaria* and *Lichina*).

Some of the simplest lichens are loose powdery associations of fungal hyphae and algal cells, but most are more compact with the fungal component forming the rigid framework of the plant and with the scattered algal cells contributing only a small amount to the total biomass. In section the outer hyphae are often packed tightly and the walls cemented together—this cortical region may be present only on the upper surface, or in the leaf-like forms on both surfaces. Internal to the cortex is the medulla, where the hyphae tend to be much looser, and in the crustose forms it is these hyphae which act as rhizoidal attaching organs. Between the cortex and medulla it is common to find the algal cells often delimited from the fungal zones (*Figure 7.1 E*) although in some lichens the arrangement is less precise with the algal component diffused throughout the medulla. Only in a few genera does the algal component comprise the greater part of the thallus whilst in all forms it is the fungal component which exerts the greatest morphogenetic influence and moulds the thallus into the numerous characteristic forms, many of them superficially resembling true fungi. Three basic morphological types can be recognized although amongst them there are many variations and inter-gradations. Some of the most obvious to students are the *fruticose* forms, with radial or flattened branching thalli either growing upright amongst moorland or Arctic vegetation, e.g. the reindeer moss, *Cladonia* (*Figure 7.1 B*), or hanging epiphytically from trees, e.g. *Usnea* (*Figure 7.1 A*) which is found both in Arctic regions and in the tropics as long greyish-green strands hanging from the branches (Old man's beard, Spanish moss). The foliose forms sometimes resemble greyish-green thalloid liverworts, e.g. *Parmelia* (*Figure 7.1 C*). The *crustose* habit is common on rock surfaces, e.g. *Lecanora* (*Figure 7.1 F*) and some of these forms are brightly coloured (yellow or orange) e.g. *Xanthoria*. They are sometimes so closely pressed to the substrate as to be difficult to remove, indeed some of them actually grow within the interstitial spaces between the substrate, e.g. between the cork layers of trees or in the pores between

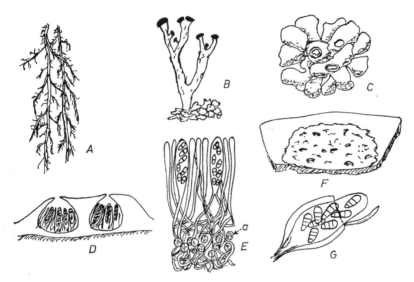

Figure 7.1. Lichens. A, Usnea; *B,* Cladonia *with apothecia at the tips of the upright branches (podetia); C,* Parmelia *with disc-like apothecia; D, E, sections through lichen apothecia; E, algal cells (a) intermingled with hyphae; F,* Lecanora *growing on rock; G, a bitunicate ascus of a lichen*

rock particles. Some are only obvious when the fruiting structures emerge above the surface. Particularly in the tropics, *crustose* or *foliose* genera are found on the upper surfaces of leaves of evergreen trees and shrubs, often in company with epiphytic algae and liverworts.

Associated with these thallus types are a range of vegetative outgrowths, many being adaptations of the thallus for vegetative reproduction, e.g. powdery loose masses (soredia) of hyphae and algae sometimes emerge through cracks on to the surface of the thallus. In other genera small papillose outgrowths (isidia) appear

93

and drop off to propagate the plant. Some lichens react to 'foreign' algae, e.g. *Nostoc* spores, which fall on to the surface—the hyphae grow out around the contaminating algae and form small structures known as cephalodia.

Until recently lichens were difficult organisms to grow and experiment with, but lately they have been grown in pure culture, and the algal and fungal components separated and cultured independently. The lichen can be fragmented and suspended in culture medium and this spread on to an agar plate where the individual algae and fungi will form colonies which can then be picked off and grown in defined media. Alternatively the individual algae can be pipetted off and washed to remove bacteria, etc., and these then grown. The fungal partner is easily isolated by growing the spores formed in the reproductive bodies of lichens. More than 30 genera of algae have been shown to be involved, some are Cyanophyta, of which *Nostoc* is the commonest, and the others Chlorophyta, of which the Chlorococcalean alga *Trebouxia* is the commonest. In the lichen thallus the algae generally grow as individual cells, but when brought into pure culture they revert to their filamentous form, e.g. *Trentepohlia*. In the lichen, the algal cells tend to be modified both physiologically and morphologically, e.g. pigment production is altered, mucilage sheaths tend not to form and production of zoospores is suppressed. As might be expected of a symbiont the algae grow better in culture on organic than inorganic media and many tend to be heterotrophic, although they do not seem to require vitamins, indeed they secrete these and polysaccharides into the media. The same alga can form the phycobiont (algal component) of many lichens, so although there are some 1500 species of lichens only approx. 30 algal genera are involved; usually only one algal species occurs in any one lichen.

In culture, the fungal partner, although it may be derived from an ascospore, only produces the asexual or imperfect stage of the life cycle. Although most of the fungi are Ascomycetes a few Basidiomycetes are known to form lichens and also some as yet imperfect fungal forms. Growth of these fungi in culture is supported by a wide range of inorganic and organic nutrients, although they do seem to require the vitamins biotin and thiamin, which in the natural state they may obtain from their algal partners. Lichens as a group produce a number of interesting organic acids and other organic compounds, but in culture they produce only a few of these or related compounds and it seems to require the presence of both the alga and the fungus for the formation of the full range of compounds.

In the normal lichen the algal cells are often penetrated by fungal haustoria, although there is some recent evidence to suggest that the haustoria are sheathed by the algal wall, i.e. they are merely invaginating the algal wall. There is, however, also contradictory evidence that the algal wall does eventually rupture.

The fungal component has never been carried through its complete sexual cycle in artificial culture—the development up to the stage of ascogonia in *Cladonia* is the furthest that has been observed. In nature the sexual reproduction of the lichens is typically that of the Ascomycetous or Basidiomycetous fungi. Flask-shaped pycnidia are formed on many lichen thalli, and as in fungi they bud off spermatia (microconidia) from the lining of conidiophores. The ascogenous system is formed as in Ascomycetes, in fruiting bodies which are either of the ascohymenial or ascolocular types (see p. 79), and likewise these are associated with unitunicate or bitunicate asci. The ascohymenial type may be apothecial or perithecial.

Classification of lichens has been a confused issue since the last century, with arguments as to whether they are merely fungi and to be absorbed into the classificatory system of that group or whether they should be maintained as a separate class—Lichenes. Most authorities maintain them as a separate group although using their fungal characters to distinguish sub-classes Ascolichenes and Hymenolichenes (i.e. with ascomycete or basidiomycete reproductive characters). The further subdivision into orders is based on the morphology of the reproductive bodies, and into classes on these characters and thallus structure. One feature of lichens which has received considerable attention and is being increasingly used in their identification and classification is their ability to form complex organic compounds which are unique to the group. Many of these substances are weak phenolic acids, the two commonest groups are depsides (esters of phenolcarboxylic acid with a phenyl benzoate

skeleton and depsidones (with a basic skeleton

). These substances react with calcium hypo-

chlorite, potassium hydroxide or *p*-phenylenediamine to give colour reactions which have been used in identification. The lichens are also one of the rare groups where microchemical tests using crystallization has been used for identification—the thallus is crushed on a microscope slide and drops of the reagent added and the slide warmed over a spirit lamp, the resulting crystals are distinctive in shape and colour.

The use of chemical tests has revealed the presence of distinct strains of lichens which although morphologically similar prove to be chemically dissimilar. A large amount of work is still required on these chemical/classificatory problems but already it is obvious that these chemical strains are sometimes geographically distributed although overlapping in certain areas.

Lichens do not have economic importance comparable to that of their algal and fungal components though they are valuable fodder in the Arctic, whilst usnic acid extracted from *Cladonia* has antibiotic properties. Litmus is extracted from a lichen, *Roccella*. They are very sensitive to air pollution, particularly to sulphur dioxide.

Classification

In the lichens this is largely a matter of relating the sexual fruiting structures to appropriate groups of the Ascomycetous fungi (and in one group to the Basidiomycetes).

Ascomycetous series. Euascomycetidae.
(*a*) Fruiting body an apothecium
Lecanorales (*Lecanora, Lichina, Peltigera, Cladonia, Parmelia, Usnea, Xanthoria*)
(*b*) Fruiting body a perithecium
Sphaeriales (*Verrucaria*)

A Loculouscomycete series also exists (*Roccella*).

Practical Study

1. Make a collection of lichens. (N.B. A geological hammer or cold chisel is necessary since you often need to collect the lichen on the actual rock.) They can be readily preserved dry in envelopes.

2. Section some of the foliose and fruticose forms and note the distribution of algae and fungi.

3. Investigate any reproductive structures—look for asci in any apothecia you find.

4. Crush some lichen thallus on a glass slide and add some acetone to extract the lichen substances. Remove the lichen and add a crystallizing reagent, e.g. glycerine–acetic acid (1 : 3) or glycerine–alcohol–water (1 : 1 : 1), put on cover glass and heat over a spirit lamp. Note the different types of crystals formed by different species.

5. Make up fresh calcium hypochlorite solution and also 10

per cent potassium hydroxide. Test the lichen thalli by adding drops of these to the cut surfaces. A positive reaction with calcium hypo-chlorite gives a red-orange colour and with potassium hydroxide a yellow colour.

Review Questions

1. What is the relationship between the algae and fungi in lichens? What effects do they have on one another?

2. Review the vegetative and reproductive types of structure found in lichens.

3. How would you set about growing the two components of lichens? What precautions would you have to take?

4. How do lichens compare with other symbiotic systems that you know? Is there always a dominant partner and is reproduction of one affected by the other?

5. What part do lichens play in the ecological system? How are they apparently adapted to life in extreme conditions?

BIBLIOGRAPHY

AHMADJIAN, V., *The Lichen Symbiosis*, Blaisdell Publishing Co., Waltham, Mass., 1967

HALE, M. E., *The Biology of Lichens*, Edward Arnold, London, 1967

8

THE BRYOPHYTA—INTRODUCTION AND LIVERWORTS

LIVERWORTS and mosses are the simplest archegoniate plants which grow on the land surface. They have minor economic significance—but are fascinating plants to study since their basic simplicity enables very detailed, satisfying studies to be made such as are impossibly time consuming on more complex plants. They have a simple alternation of a gametophytic phase (the vegetative plant) with a 'parasitic' sporophytic phase (the capsule), with the dispersal unit (spore) and its germling (the protonema) forming intermediate phases (*Figures 8.1–9.3*). In some systems of classification the term 'metaphyta' is used for all groups above the algal/fungal series; the 'metaphyta' are then divided into Bryophyta and Tracheophyta, a distinction based on the absence or presence of distinct vascular strands. This is a useful concept but one which is over-ridden by the archegoniate status of plants in both groups, and reproductive structures are usually given more weight than vegetative structures in classificatory systems.

The most striking features not encountered in the algae are the formation of sterile wall layers around the gametangia and the high degree of differentiation of the sporophytes accompanied by reduction in photosynthetic capacity. The antheridia are simple sac-like structures with an outer sterile wall and usually a stalk consisting of a few cells (*Figures 8.1 H, 8.2 B, J* and *8.3 E*). The internal, fertile cells form biflagellate rather elongate gametes which require a film of water to swim in and reach the archegonia. The latter are shorter and more massively stalked or sunken within the thallus (e.g. *Anthoceros*). The base is somewhat swollen and often several cells thick, enclosing the egg cell. Above, it is drawn out into a long neck of many tiers of cells and enclosing a series of neck canal cells which degenerate prior to fertilization. Both antheridia and archegonia are basically short filaments growing by means of a single apical cell—the former expanding at the apex and the latter at the base. In the antheridia a central cell divides repeatedly to form the antherozooid mother cells surrounded by the sterile wall cells. In the archegonium, however, the central cell gives rise to two cells, one of which continues division to form the neck canal cells whilst the other only divides once more to form the sterile venter canal cell and the egg cell. Variations on these forms occur throughout the remainder of the lower plants.

Yet another feature of this group is the basic conservatism of the organs; they differ in detail but vegetatively there are only three basic growth forms, (*a*) a parenchymatous thallus (*Figures 8.1* and *8.2*), (*b*) a dorsiventral leafy thallus with two rows of lateral leaves and a third modified row of 'underleaves' (*Figures 8.3* and *8.4*), (*c*) an upright or creeping plant (*Figures 9.1–9.3*) with spirally arranged leaves (occasionally heteromorphic and sometimes two-ranked).

Most Bryophytes are small plants creeping along the ground or erect and a few centimetres high. They often occur in dense patches, but only rarely form dominant vegetation, e.g. in *Sphagnum* bogs. Even in temperate climates some grow epiphytically on tree trunks, whilst in the humid tropics they grow over both bark and leaf surfaces. In mountainous regions they grow on apparently inhospitable rock surfaces and crevices, and even in city streets a few species can be found in the cracks between paving stones. They extend from the edges of snowfields to the tropics, but are infrequent in hot desert regions and have not penetrated seawards beyond the fringes of the marine habitats. Many species have precise ecological requirements and are valuable indicators of certain habitat conditions.

With experience, mosses and liverworts are easily distinguishable, but general rules for recognition are difficult. The clearest distinction is in the structure of the sporophytes—a relatively simple spherical sac in the liverworts but a complex, usually cylindrical photosynthetic structure in the mosses, with a tubular mass of spore tissue around a central sterile columella and with a series of 'iris-diaphragm-like' teeth at the apical end (*Figures 8.1 B* and *9.3 C*).

Three classes are included in the Bryophyta: Hepaticopsida (liverworts), Anthoceropsida (a small group of thalloid forms, see p. 108) and the Bryopsida (mosses). The use of the suffix -opsida for a class of plants above the algae (which use -phyceae) and fungi (-mycetes) is laid down in the rules of botanical nomenclature—this in no way alters the concept of these groups, and you will encounter them in some books as Hepaticae, Hepaticales, etc.

Hepaticopsida

The spores of liverworts are small (5 μ to 150 μ), vary in colour from pale yellowish green/green-brown and are released in great numbers on bursting of the capsule. Occasionally they remain together in tetrads as formed in the capsule at meiosis, but usually they separate. Each spore is usually unicellular and the wall is variously ornamented with fine punctures, spines or ridges. It sometimes retains the tetrahedral shape which results from the

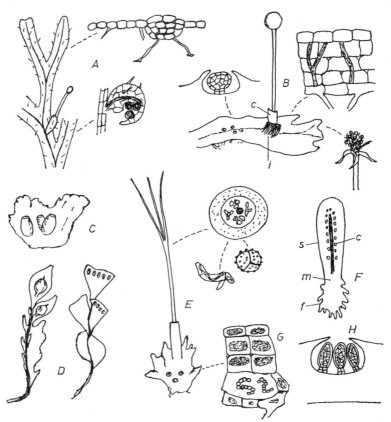

Figure 8.1. Thalloid liverworts. A, Metzgeria, *segment of the thallus with a sporogonium, transverse section and branch containing antheridia; B,* Pellia. *Plant with antheridia and mature sporogonium surrounded at base by the involucre (i) and calyptra (c). Sections through depression in thallus, containing an antheridium, and one showing the bars of material traversing the thallus. Below right, a dehisced sporogonium; C,* Sphaerocarpus *with cups on the surface which contain either antheridia or archegonia; D,* Riella. *Female plant with sporogonia on left and male plant with antheridia on right; E,* Anthoceros *plant with antheridial pits on the thallus below the ripe sporogonium. On the right a transverse section of the sporogonium showing the central columella and below an elator and a spore; G, section of* Anthoceros *thallus with single large chloroplasts in the cells and filaments of a blue-green alga in cavities; F, section of young sporogonium, spores (s), columella (c), foot (f), basal meristem (m); H, section through an antheridial pit with three antheridia*

cleavage of a sphere into four equal solid bodies, and this gives the spore three triangular faces, derived from the internal cleavage planes and an outer convex face, which is part of the external surface of the spore mother cell. In *Pellia* (*Figure 8.1 B*) the spore divides prior to release, thus commencing the formation of the protonema whilst still in the capsule. Dispersal of the spores is probably mainly by wind currents close to the surface of the substrate, but undoubtedly small insects, arachnids, etc., play a part in dissemination and the very great geographic range of many species suggests ease of transport.

The protonemal stage is generally not conspicuous and indeed generally ignored in the description of liverworts. Nevertheless it is a distinct phase in the growth cycle. The spore wall splits, the contents bulge out and cell divisions occur to produce a small filiform or sub-globose mass of undifferentiated parenchymatous tissue (*Figure 8.3 A*). A cell at the periphery or on a side branch differentiates to form an apical meristematic cell and subsequent divisions of this give rise to the form of the normal vegetative plant. This is, with few exceptions (e.g. Haplomitrales), a dorsiventral structure, i.e. creeping and differing in development on the upper (dorsal) and lower (ventral) surfaces. This dorsiventrality is traceable back to the segmentation of the apical cell—one of the easiest to study is *Metzgeria* (*Figure 8.1 A*).

The two basic types are thalloid (e.g. *Pellia* and *Conocephalum*) and foliose (e.g. *Lophocolea* and *Frullania*). In the former the branched thallus is either rosette-like or tongue-shaped. In *Pellia* the thallus is relatively undifferentiated with a thickened mid-rib region strengthened by internal bands (*Figure 8.1 B*). The dorsal surface bears simple rhizoids, these being merely prolongations of the epidermal cells. *Conocephalum* (a genus close to *Marchantia* but more readily obtainable growing on damp stone, particularly on bridgeworks over flowing water) is much more complex—on the dorsal surface a hexagonal pattern is visible, each mesh having a central pore (*Figure 8.2 E*). The pores are complex (in *Marchantia* forming 'barrel pores', *Figure 8.2 C*) and open into underlying photosynthetic chambers, the supporting walls of which form the hexagonal meshwork. The chambers are lined with a basal system of branching photosynthetic cells culminating in colourless flask-shaped cells (*Figure 8.2 I*). The tissue beneath this photosynthetic zone is parenchyma with few chloroplasts. Conspicuous oil bodies are often present in the cells. Along the ventral surface a series of small 'leaves' occurs on either side of the mid-line—they are plates of cells, one cell thick and frequently with purple cell sap. These are the amphigastria

Figure 8.2. Marchantiales. A, Riccia *thallus and diagrammatic cross-section; B*, Marchantia, *part of thallus with gemma cup and antheridiophore and on right, half section through the head of antheridiophore; C, female thallus of* Marchantia *and section through archegoniophore with maturing sporogonium. Note 'barrel' pores in upper region of the archegoniophore and a single pore system enlarged above; D, gemma cup and gemma of* Marchantia: *E,* Conocephalum *with archegoniophore; F, undersurface of* Conocephalum *showing amphigastria and rhizoids; G, longitudinal section of young archegoniophore of* Conocephalum *with developing sporogonia; H, diagrammatic longitudinal section of* Targionia *showing the archegonia on the lower surface of the thallus; I, section through a pore region of* Conocephalum, *note photosynthetic filaments, peg and smooth rhizoids and amphigastrium; J, diagrammatic section through an antheridial cushion of* Conocephalum; *K, surface view of latter*

and are usually obscured by the dense growth of rhizoids—some smooth and others with small internal proliferations of the wall (the peg rhizoids, *Figure 8.2 I*). In the related genus *Riccia* the pores are absent, and the photosynthetic region is a system of anastomosing filaments or a system of upright filaments (*Figure 8.2 A*). In this genus some species grow as floating aquatics.

The antheridia and archegonia are often sunken within the thallus in these genera. Thus in *Pellia* they are in small pits scattered around the mid-dorsal line some way behind the apex—each is a short-stalked sac protected by a slightly arched swelling of the thallus at the centre of which is a pore. In *Metzgeria* they are contained within small sac-like branches arising from the ventral surface (*Figure 8.1 A*). The more complex thalli of the Marchantiales produce special structures bearing the antheridia (antheridiophores), and these may simply be cushion-like swellings on the dorsal surface of the thallus (e.g. *Conocephalum, Figure 8.2 K*) or they may be stalked out-growths within which the antheridia are sunken in pits (e.g. *Marchantia, Figure 8.2 B*). Archegonia are formed from superficial cells behind the apex, either on the main axis or on branches. Continued growth from the apical cells thrusts the archegonial initial cells on to the dorsal surface, e.g. *Riccia* and *Pellia*, or on to the ventral surface, e.g. *Targionia* (*Figure 8.2 H*). Although superficial in origin during development the archegonia are usually protected by the upgrowth of surrounding tissue. In *Marchantia* the branch bearing the archegonia bends upwards to form the archegoniophore and expansion of the central region pushes the developing archegonia to the underside so that in this and several other genera, e.g. *Conocephalum, Reboulia, Preissia* and *Lunnularia* they hang with the neck of the archegonium pointing downwards (*Figure 8.2 C, E, G.*) The apex of the archegoniophore dichotomizes to varying degrees in the different genera and is morphologically similar to the thallus, with characteristic pores, assimilating chambers and on the ventral side scales and rhizoids—these are merely a reflection of its branching nature.

The development of the sporophyte generation is completed within the enlarged archegonial wall, now termed the calyptra, and its emergence is merely a process of cell elongation. In the *Conocephalum* type, fertilization and initial development occurs whilst the archegoniophore is still a short structure sitting upon the thallus (*Figure 8.2 G*), and then the stalk of the archegoniophore elongates rapidly carrying the sporangia above the surface of the thallus. In these genera the stalk of the capsule is short, elongating only sufficiently to project the sporogonium *down* from beneath the lobes of the archegoniophore. The developing archegonia and sporophytes are protected by outgrowths (involucre) from the undersurface of the archegoniophore—around each sporogonium in *Lunnularia* and around each row in *Marchantia*. The latter genus has additional protection from individual sheaths (pseudoperianths) growing around each developing sporogonium—thus giving three investments, calyptra, pseudoperianth and involucre.

The development and form of the sporophyte generation is similar to that of foliose liverworts (see below), except in *Riccia* and allied genera, where the zygote undergoes a series of divisions

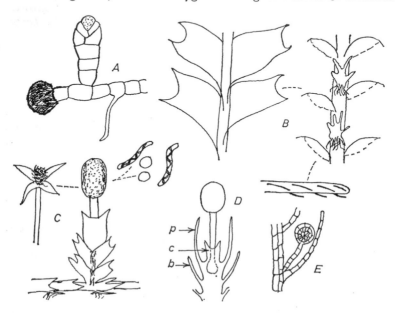

Figure 8.3. Leafy liverworts. A, development of a leafy liverwort on the protonema growing from a spore; B, Lophocolea *from the dorsal side (left) and from the ventral side (right). Note the decurrent leaf bases and the bilobed underleaves. Below, a diagram of the angle of insertion of the leaves in relation to the stem apex, showing a succubous arrangement; C, sporophytic branch of a leafy liverwort, dehisced sporogonium, spores and elators; D, diagrammatic section through a sporogonium (p = perianth, c = calyptra, b = bracts); E, antheridium of a leafy liverwort in the axil of a leaf*

to form a spherical capsule, the only sterile part of which is the wall. No elators are formed—sterile cells within the central mass merely breaking down to form a nutrient layer around the spores. The capsule wall may be retained or it may be absorbed, in which case the spores lie free in the old archegonial wall. No special mechanism of dehiscence exists—the spores are shed on decay of the thallus.

The foliose genera are very much more numerous and common

on soil, decaying wood, bark, leaves, etc. Basically these are rod-like thalli with three spirally arranged rows of very thin leaves. The leaves are generally dimorphic in that the ventral row is small, often bilobed, adpressed to the stem and frequently somewhat obscured by rhizoids, whilst the other two rows of leaves are extended laterally on either side of the stem (*Figure 8.3 B*). The 'leaves' are usually only one cell thick except at the base in some species. The cells contain numerous lenticular chloroplasts and variously shaped oil bodies. Cell walls are often conspicuously thickened at the corners to form the so-called 'trigones' (*Figure 8.4 E*).

To understand the morphology of these 'leafy liverworts' it is necessary to consider the segmentation from the apical cell (*Figure 8.4 F, G*). This is three-sided, the lower side giving rise to the tissue from which the underleaves form and the two lateral segments giving rise to the lateral leaves. The segments are cut off in a spiral sequence and each segment divides into two outer cells and one inner cell—the outer cells divide to form the leaf and the bifid nature of this leaf is often derivable from these two cells. The inner cell divides to add tissue to the stem. In most genera the leaves are incised to some degree (*Figures 8.3 B, 8.4*), but in the extreme cases there are two segments of unequal size—the smaller of which may be modified to form a water storage organ, e.g. in *Frullania* (*Figure 8.4 C*). As can be seen from the diagrams, either the ventral (often termed antical—meaning in front or above if the stem is creeping) or dorsal segments (often termed postical) of the lateral leaves may be developed more than the other (*Figure 8.4 B, C, G*). The leaves are always stalkless and the junction with the stem is often extended backwards and is at an angle to the vertical due to the unequal growth of the dorsal and ventral sides of the stem. This angle is extremely important in the classification of the genera and leaves which point forwards so that the upper edge overlaps the lower edge of the leaf above are termed 'incubous' (*Figure 8.4 C*); the opposite arrangement is 'succubous' (*Figure 8.3 B*). A few genera have the leaves equally developed and the stem is upright, rather like that of a moss (e.g. *Marsupella, Figure 8.4 D*).

Branching may occur at the apex or it may be intercalary. In the former, new three-sided apical cells are formed by cleavage in the leaf of initial cells—usually in the ventral half, thus eliminating the ventral (i.e. postical) lobe of the leaf (*Figure 8.4 F*). The *Radula* type is interesting since it does not result in any curtailment of the leaf development (*Figure 8.4 G*). The intercalary type, in which branches arise from a point behind the apex, are almost always due to the formation of an apical cell in the ventral segment.

The antheridia and archegonia are never sunken in tissue and are usually in groups—the commonest arrangement being of antheridia on one branch and archegonia on another, but numerous variations exist. The antheridia are formed from cells in the dorsal region of the leaves (only rarely in the axes of the underleaves) and their formation in no way involves the apical cell of the branch (*Figure 8.3 E*). Sometimes the protective leaves (perigonia) are unmodified vegetative leaves, but the antical lobe is often somewhat modified to protect the antheridia.

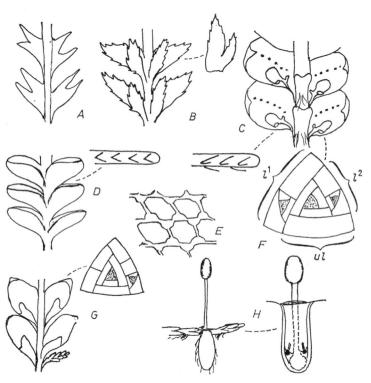

Figure 8.4. Leafy liverworts. A, Cephalozia; *B, bilobed leaves of* Diplophyllum; *C,* Frullania, *showing modified postical lobes, underleaves and row of coloured cells across the antical lobe. Below left, a diagram of the leaf insertion—incubous arrangement of leaves; D,* Marsupella *and right, the transverse leaf insertion; E, thickened 'trigones' in the angles of cells of a liverwort leaf; F, diagram of the apical segmentation and origins of two lateral branches in* Frullania. *Apical cells dotted. (l^1, l^2) the segments giving rise to the two lateral leaves, (ul.) the segment giving rise to the underleaf; G,* Radula *with a side branch and on right diagram of the apical segmentation and origin of a branch system without the elimination of the lower lobe of the lateral leaf; H,* Calypogeia, *with a sporogonium arising from a marsupium. Diagrammatically on right, note archegonia in the basal region of the marsupium*

The archegonia, in contrast to the antheridia, are borne at the apex of either the main stem or a side branch and the apical cell is often used in their formation, e.g. *Frullania*, where a single archegonium arises from this cell. In other genera the apical cell and adjacent surface cells develop into archegonia—forming up to a 100 in an apical cluster in species of *Lophocolea*. The archegonial branch bears normal leaves at the base but nearer the apex the leaves are progressively modified—the altered, often enlarged lateral leaves being termed bracts and the altered underleaves bracteoles; collectively these form the perichaetium which may be more or less fused at the base (*Figure 8.3 C, D*). In addition to this protection, in some genera a tubular outgrowth is also developed from the basal part of the developing archegonium and grows up to form an often very distinctive structure—the perianth (*Figure 8.3 D*). It is formed independently of fertilization of the archegonia. In some species the perianth is clearly a tripartite structure, originating from three sectors around the base of the archegonium and thus traceable to the three spiral cutting faces derived from the apical cell. It thus appears as three fused leaves. In other genera, only the lateral segments are utilized in the formation of the perianth. One further development of the archegonial branch in some genera is the proliferation (e.g. *Calypogeia*) of *stem* tissue on the *ventral* side to form a positively geotropic growth, which may even bury itself in the substratum and be provided with rhizoids. The archegonia are then found buried in the base of this structure, which is termed the marsupium or perigynium (*Figure 8.4 H*).

The embryonic sporogonium develops as a tiered structure with the sporogenous tissue confined to the apical part and surrounded by the enlarged archegonial wall, which is initially only one cell thick. The basal regions are sterile and form the potential seta and absorbing foot. As this structure grows the archegonial wall (venter) also undergoes further divisions and expands as a protective layer (calyptra) around the developing embryo. The foot penetrates to a varying extent into the stem tissue. Development of an embryo with the apex growing outwards in the direction of the neck of the archegonium is known as exoscopic and is common to all Bryophyta. The seta and capsule are formed whilst still surrounded by the calyptra and the extension of the seta is not achieved by growth in the sense of cell division, but is merely a rapid elongation of the pre-existing cells. Unlike the seta of mosses it is hyaline and without conspicuous wall thickenings. Commonly the capsule wall is two cells thick but in some genera, e.g. *Plagiochila*, it is as many as seven to eight cells thick. Frequently the wall cells are strengthened

107

by band-shaped thickenings and they often contain chloroplasts, although they can perform only a limited amount of photosynthesis. The wall generally splits along four radii from the apex. The sporogenous tissue forms tetrads of spores and also elongate sterile cells internally strengthened with spiral bands of thickening (elators, *Figure 8.3 C*). The latter may lie loose amongst the spore mass or be attached, e.g. in *Frullania*, where they are stretched from apex to base and anchored at both ends.

Asexual reproduction is fairly widespread amongst liverworts. In some leafy species cells are budded off from the leaf apices. Half moon-shaped gemmae cups are formed in *Lunnularia* and round cups with serrated edges in *Marchantia* (*Figure 8.2 D*)—these cups contain numerous multicellular plate-like gemmae which develop from superficial cells at the base of the cups. These outgrowths initiate apical cells in two lateral indentations and it is from these cells that new plants are formed. Amongst the gemmae in the cups are mucilaginous glands which introduce mucilage amongst the gemmae and it is said that swelling of this breaks the gemmae off their stalks.

Classification

The arrangement into major groups has been relatively fixed for a considerable time and changes are of a relatively minor nature. Additional notes are added where it is considered helpful, especially on small groups not considered in detail above.

Anthoceropsida (*Figure 8.1 E–H*).

Antherocerotales. Gametophytes of rosette-like branches, simple parenchyma with a single large chloroplast in each cell. No oil bodies. Smooth rhizoids. Antheridia sunken in pits on the dorsal surface and often branching from the base. Archegonia similarly sunken. Sporogonia consisting of a rhizoidal foot region and a tubular 'capsule' with a multilayered wall containing primitive stomata, a central sterile columella and a dome-shaped mass of spore tissue. Elators multicellular and branched. Dehiscence by two slits leaving the central columella standing. The whole structure growing by means of a basal meristem and forming a grass leaf-like structure several inches long in *Anthoceros*. Only three other genera, *Megaceros*, *Dendroceros* and *Notothylas*.

Hepaticopsida

Jungermanniales. Gametophytes leafy. Numerous chloroplasts

and oil globules in the cells. Rhizoids smooth. Sporogonia spherical or egg-shaped without columella or stomata. Wall mostly of several layers splitting into four segments. Leaves in three rows, one row of which is often small (underleaves). Archegonia apical and utilizing the apical cell. Developing sporogonium protected by the fusion of the upper leaves. The largest grouping with over 100 genera. (*Calypogeia, Frullania, Lophocolea, Marsupella, Plagiochila, Radula.*)

Metzgeriales. Thallose or with irregular leaf-like projections. Archegonia mainly dorsal and not involving the apical cell of the branch. A small group containing approximately 20 genera. (*Pellia, Metzgeria.*)

Calobryales. A small order with only two genera.

Sphaerocarpales. Gametophyte thallose (*Sphaerocarpus, Figure 8.1 C*) or with indistinct lamina (*Riella, Figure 8.1 I*). Rhizoids smooth. Archegonia and antheridia dorsal in flask-shaped structures (*Sphaerocarpus*) or archegonia in pear-shaped structures and antheridia in margins of wings of laminae (*Riella*). Spherical capsule on a short stalk. Wall of capsule one cell layer thick. Only two genera—*Riella* is aquatic and *Sphaerocarpus* grows on soil.

Marchantiales. Gametophyte thallose often of complex form with photosynthetic and storage portions, often chambered and with pores. Oil bodies in special cells. Smooth- and peg-rhizoids. Archegonia and antheridia sunken in the thallus, segments of which are often raised above the surface as outgrowths (archegoniophores and antheridiophores). Sporogonia spherical or egg-shaped with or without short setae. Single layered wall breaking into segments or releasing a cap on dehiscence. A well defined group with approximately 20 genera. (*Riccia, Targionia, Conocephalum, Lunnularia, Preissia, Reboulia, Marchantia, Corsinia.*)

Practical Study

1. Collect as many 'leafy' and 'thallose' liverworts as you can. They are not scarce—look particularly on the soil, decaying wood, tree trunks, etc., in damp woodland. They often also grow on the soil of plant pots in cool greenhouses, e.g. those used for ferns. *Lunnularia* is very common in greenhouses.

2. Study carefully the arrangement of leaves on the 'leafy' forms. Determine whether they are incubous or succubous. Look for the underleaves and illustrate their form and compare with the lateral leaves.

3. Look for antheridia, archegonia and gemmae—they are all more common than you might think.

4. Cut transverse sections of 'thallose' forms and look for pores and photosynthetic filaments. Cut thin slices off the surfaces of the forms with 'polygonal markings' and see the surface view of the pores—generally visible around the edges of the section.

5. Dissect the rhizoids from forms such as *Lunnularia* and *Conocephalum* and mount for microscopic observation. Are they all the same? Look carefully for the amphigastria along the undersides of the 'mid-rib'.

6. The capsules of most liverworts are very delicate—compare the stalks with those of mosses. Squash the capsules and draw the spores and elators. Are the spores unicellular? Has the capsule wall any special features?

7. Attempt to grow spores on agar, in liquid culture or on moist soil. Many liverworts can also be cultured from segments of the thallus laid out on soil and kept moist—but not flooded, because of fungal infection. How can you minimize this?

8. Antheridiophores and archegoniophores can be sectioned longitudinally during early stages of growth. *Conocephalum* is very suitable for this—the capsules will be too mature if the archegoniophore has elongated, therefore cut the material when it shows only the conical protuberances just sitting on the thallus.

Review Questions

1. Review the distinguishing characteristics of the 'leafy' and 'thallose' series of liverworts.

2. What features lead to the subdivision of the 'thallose' forms into three main series?

3. To what extent is the sporophytic generation an independent entity?

4. The simplest 'liverworts' are no more complex than many algae. Why then are they ranked in a higher posit?

5. How is dispersal of the spore achieved? Is the development and form of the sporophytes related in any way to the ecology of the various genera?

BIBLIOGRAPHY

BOWER, F. O., *Primitive Land Plants—also Known as the Archegoniatae,* Macmillan, London, 1935 (reprinted 1959)

PARIHAR, N. S., *An Introduction to Embryophyta*, Vol. I, *Bryophyta* (4th edn), Central Book Depot, Allahabad, 1964

SMITH, G. M., *Cryptogamic Botany*, Vol. II (2nd edn), McGraw-Hill, New York, 1955

WATSON, E. V., *The Structure and Life of Bryophytes*, Hutchinson, London, 1967

9

THE BRYOPHYTA—MOSSES

THE mosses (Bryopsida) are even less variable in vegetative morphology than the liverworts. They all consist of a solid axis of cells bearing spirally arranged leaves. Nevertheless some are upright and others creeping and these latter are sometimes superficially like leafy liverworts. The capsules, however, are usually borne on wiry stalks and elongated and often carry up the upper half of the broken calyptra. They also have a very distinctive dehiscence mechanism and all these points clearly distinguish the mosses from the liverworts.

The spores of mosses vary enormously in size (5–200 μ) and in ornamentation. On release from the capsule they germinate to form a much more extensive protonemal system than that of the liverworts. The protonema is generally a much branched filamentous 'algal'-like growth characterized by oblique cross walls and discoid chromatophores. In a few genera the protonema is the normal vegetative stage and leafy branches are only formed prior to the formation of archegonia and antheridia, but normally buds develop on the protonema from the basal cells of branches (*Figure 9.2 D*) and grow into leafy shoots. In a few genera, the most notable of which are *Sphagnum* and *Andreaea*, the protonema is a parenchymatous structure resembling a thallose liverwort and buds are initiated from cells at the edge (*Figure 9.1 B*).

In the vast majority of mosses the apical cell of the bud on the protonema lays down three walls to form a three-sided apical cell, and from the three lateral faces, cells are produced in a spiral and these form the basic rows of leaf initials. The outer face does not give rise to tissues (*Figure 9.2 G*). In only a few genera (e.g. the aquatic moss *Fontinalis, Figure 9.3 E*) is the segmentation undisturbed to give precisely three rows of leaves (tristichous)—in most genera torsion of the stem or displacement of the leaves soon results in other arrangements. Some genera have a two-sided apical cell and then the arrangement of leaves is in two rows (distichous), e.g. *Fissidens* (*Figure 9.3 F*). The leaves of mosses are comparable to those of liverworts in having no stalk, often being one cell thick and growing from a two-sided apical cell, but differ in that there is a distinct mid-rib in many genera, frequent elongation of the cells and the formation of

112

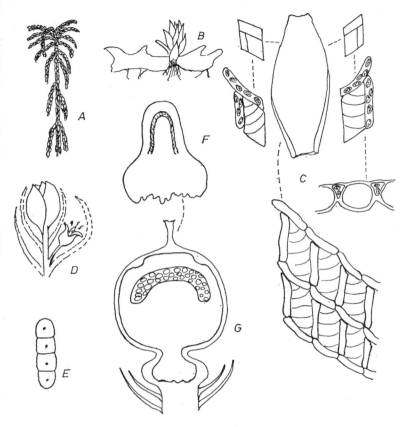

Figure 9.1. Sphagnum. *A, apex of a plant; B, thalloid protonema with a bud; C, leaf form and the segmentation of cells on either side of the mid-line to form chlorophyllose and hyaline cells. Below, a cross-section of the leaf showing one arrangement of the chlorophyllose cells between the hyaline and the appearance of part of a mature leaf (without chloroplasts drawn); D, a fertile branch with the leaves stripped off to reveal a dehisced antheridium; E, the four-celled stage of the* Sphagnum *embryo; F, a latter stage of the embryonic sporogonium showing the basal foot, columella and dome-shaped spore tissue; G, longitudinal section of an almost mature sporogonium*

special marginal cells. Occasionally they also form photosynthetic lamellae as outgrowths on the upper surface of the leaf (*Figure 9.3 G*) and in some there is marked heteromorphy of the cells, especially in the basal regions. Dimorphic development of the leaves occurs in some tropical mosses, with rows of small leaves lying along the stem and larger rows of lateral leaves—these are not likely to be confused with liverworts—in fact they have a superficial resemblance to some

113

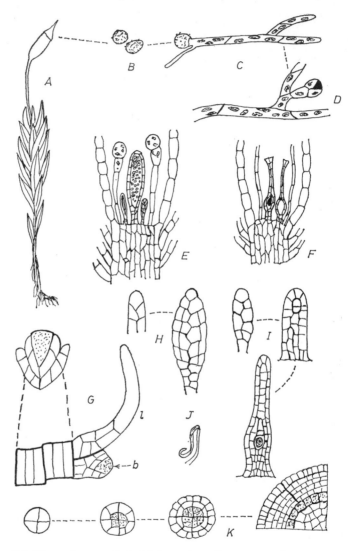

Figure 9.2. Mosses. A, a moss plant with sporogonium; B, moss spores; C, protonema growing from a spore; D, part of a protonema with a bud arising from the basal cell of a branch; E, longitudinal section of a male plant with antheridia and paraphyses; F, similar of a female plant; G, diagram of the segmentation from an apical cell and the growth of a leaf (l) and bud (b); H, stages in the development of an antheridium; I, stages in the development of an archegonium; J, antherozooid, K, diagrammatic sections through a developing sporogonium, potential spore tissue dotted

114

small species of *Selaginella* (see p. 130). In some species the main stem leaves and branch leaves differ somewhat in size and form, e.g. *Sphagnum* and many species of the section *Hypnobryales*. One of the most striking leaf modifications occurs in *Sphagnum*, where each cell which is derived from the two-sided apical cuts off two segments— an upper and an outer—and these develop into the chloroplast containing chlorophyllose cells and the other cell of the triad lays down spiral bands of thickening to become the water storing hyaline cell (*Figure 9.1 C*).

The stem of the moss plant is formed from cells cut off parallel to the internal face of the leaf initials. In *Fontinalis* there are two such cells which then undergo further divisions (*Figure 9.2 G*). Branches are formed from the basal halves of the outer stem sectors and therefore lie beneath the leaves and not in the axil. The leaf itself is not in any way modified by the emergence of a branch as opposed to most liverworts. The anchoring system of mosses consists of multicellular rhizoids growing from the stem and often clothing the stem for some distance, e.g. *Aulacomnium* and *Polytrichum*. The only other structures borne on the stems are small leaf-like objects often much divided and termed paraphyllia, e.g. in *Hylocomium* and *Thuidium*—their function is not clear (*Figure 9.3 I*).

The archegonia and antheridia (*Figure 9.2 H, J*) are always terminal, either on the main axis (acrocarpus) or on side branches (pleurocarpus) and the apical cell is sacrificed. In a few genera, e.g. *Polytrichum*, it is common to find new shoots springing out of the centres of the antheridial clusters. The sex organs are usually borne on fairly massive multicellular stalks and are in many aspects the most elaborate amongst the lower plants, since those of the Pteridophytes are often sunken within the tissue and apparently reduced in form. The arrangement of antheridia and archegonia is diverse, e.g. they may be found on separate plants (*dioecious*) or on the same plant (*monoecious*), where they may be in separate receptacles, separated by a few leaves or completely mixed within a single receptacle. The receptacle is generally the flattened apex of a branch and is surrounded by modified leaves—so-called perichaetial leaves around the archegonial and mixed receptacles and perigonial leaves around the antheridia. These protective leaves are not fused together as in many liverworts. In addition there are filamentous outgrowths —paraphyses—which grow up between the sex organs and separate them (*Figure 9.2 E, F*). *Sphagnum* is an exception in that although the the archegonia are formed at the apices of small club-shaped branches, the antheridia are delicate structures on long stalks in the axils of the leaves (*Figure 9.1 D*), (c.f. those of leafy liverworts).

115

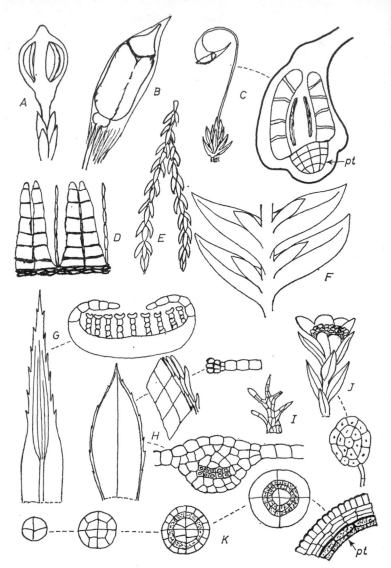

Figure 9.3. Mosses. A, sporogonium of Andreaea; *B, sporogonium of* Polytrichum *with torn calyptra carried up as a covering; C, part of* Funaria *with sporogonium also carrying a calyptra. On right, a diagrammatic longitudinal section of the sporogonium with the developing peristome teeth (pt); D, inner and outer peristome teeth of a moss sporogonium; E,* Fontinalis *with three distinct rows of leaves; F,* Fissidens *with two rows of leaves, formed into a two-lipped pocket on the upper side; G,* Polytrichum *leaf, with section on right showing the photosynthetic lamellae in section; H, moss leaf with thickened marginal cells—edge enlarged and on right in section to show the multiple layers at the margin and in the mid-rib; I, one of the paraphyllia of a moss of the Hypnobryales; J,* Tetraphis—*apex with a gemma cup and below a single gemma; K, development of the sporogonium in the peristome region to show the cutting off of segments to form the peristome teeth (pt), cells destined for teeth shaded*

These *Sphagnum* antheridia dehisce by splitting of the apex, whereas most moss antheridia have a single cell or a few apical cells modified to form an operculum which is thrown off as the antheridia swell and dehisce to release the biflagellate male gametes.

Polarity of the embryo is established from the first division of the zygote, which is transverse to the long axis of the archegonium, as in liverworts. Three cell divisions produce an elongate embryo of four cells (e.g. *Figure 9.1 F*) after which division in other planes occurs and the embryo tends to grow from apical and basal meristematic cells. The lower zone forms the anchoring and absorbing foot region and the upper zone the moss capsule itself. As in liverworts, considerable development occurs within the enlarged archegonium, which itself undergoes cell division to accommodate the embryo, but growth continues after rupture of the archegonium. The upper half of the archegonium is carried up on the tip of the capsule in the form of a calyptra (*Figure 9.3 B, C*). The lower enlarged half of the archegonium is sometimes termed the vaginula. Like many plant structures the moss capsule is a highly defined unit, since the sequence of cell divisions is extremely precise; this is most clearly seen in the formation of the unique peristome derived from rows of cells cut from the original quadrants, therefore the number of teeth are four or multiples of four. This development is best seen in transverse section, where at an early stage an internal group of cells can be recognized forming the endothecium (*Figure 9.2 K*) in which subsequent cell division is somewhat irregular, giving rise to an external ring of sporogenous tissue often two cells thick, and an internal sterile columella. Externally the cell divisions are more precisely orientated in the anticlinal and periclinal planes, i.e. at right angles to the circumference and parallel to the circumference respectively. Close to the apex the development of the peristome can be followed; first, two anticlinal walls completely divide the embryo, but the next four do not penetrate the endothecium, they separate an outer ring of eight cells. Continued periclinal divisions give rise to a concentric series of cell layers and anticlinal divisions of the two inner concentric rings define the number of 'teeth' of the inner and outer peristome. External to this the cells form the operculum and its epidermis. In longitudinal section the peristome forms a cone-shaped structure beneath the operculum (*Figure 9.3 C*). The latter is separated from the lower cylindrical part of the capsule by a group of enlarged thin-walled cells—the annulus. The epidermal cells of the operculum and of the capsule are thickened and as the capsule dries a split occurs in the annulus and the operculum is thrown off. The peristomal layers have wall thickening material deposited on the periclinal walls and sometimes on the longitudinal anticlinal walls, whilst the vertical anticlinal walls remain unthickened, at least along the lines of division, giving rise to the 16, 32, or 64 segments which will form the teeth of the peristome (*Figure 9.3 D*). The anticlinal cell walls between the outer and inner peristome layers breaks and the inner and outer teeth are then free— their number is not necessarily the same in each layer, this depends on the number of anticlinal divisions in each layer (see *Figure 9.3 K*). The inner peristome does not move to any great extent, but the teeth of the outer peristome move inwards in moist weather and 'close the capsule', and outwards in dry weather. In many species the outer teeth alternate with the inner, and on closing they slip in between the inner teeth and touch the spore mass, picking up spores which are carried out when the peristome teeth move outwards again. A few mosses are cleistocarpic and have no peristome or operculum, but split irregularly to release the spores—often large and few in number. In these genera the columella may remain or it may be reabsorbed, e.g. in *Archidium*.

The main body of the capsule is cylindrical and often curved. It is derived from concentric rings of cells formed by the series of periclinal and anticlinal cleavages which give rise to the endothecium, spore tissue and amphithecium. Profuse development of chloroplasts in the radial rows of cells in the amphithecium and the separation of the cells to yield spaces amongst the cells results in a tissue very similar to the multiple palisade tissue of some angiosperm leaves. The epidermis has stomata of fairly complex structure which parallel some of the developments seen in higher plants, e.g. sinking below the surface and differential thickening of walls. The transitional region between the spore bearing section and the seta is termed the apophysis and is also photosynthetic. Sections of the seta of mosses show a much more complex structure than that of liverworts, often with external rows of thickened cells and an internal ring of thickened cells resembling the endodermis of higher plants.

Three rather special types of capsule are encountered in the Sphagnales, Andreaeales and Polytrichales. The first two have dome-shaped masses of spore tissue and are borne on the ends of short pseudopodia formed of gametophyte tissue—*Sphagnum* species dehisce by an explosive ejection of the operculum caused by an increase in internal air pressure as the capsule shrinks (*Figure 9.1 G*). In *Andreaea* four longitudinal splits appear in the capsule (*Figure 9.3 A*). In *Polytrichum* there is a single ring of rigid, short peristome teeth, and the flattish apex of the capsule is covered by a layer of

118

tissue stretched across from the tips of the peristome teeth like the skin of a drum (the epiphragma), and the spores are shed through the spaces between adjacent teeth. The teeth are composed of several concentric rows of cells thickened to form fibres.

Vegetative reproduction by gemmae is common amongst mosses —these clusters of cells or multicellular bodies are usually formed on leaves and only occasionally in special apical clusters, e.g. the stalked gemmae of *Tetraphis* (*Figure 9.3 J*). Cut segments of leaves and stems can also regenerate new plants.

Classification

The main subdivisions of the Bryopsida have not changed since early investigations but minor changes and alterations in the status of the groups have and will continue to be made. A division into a series of sub-classes seems to be adequate.

Sphagnidae
    Sphagnales (*Sphagnum*)
Andreaeidae
    Andreaeales (*Andreaea*)
Bryidae. The subdivision of these depends very much on the structure of the peristome of the sporophyte.
    Archidiales (*Archidium*)
    Fissidentales (*Fissidens*)
    Funariales (*Funaria*)
    Tetraphidales (*Tetraphis*)
    Eubryales (*Mnium, Aulacomnium*)
    Isobryales (*Fontinalis*)
    Hypnobryales (*Hylocomium, Thuidium*)
Polytrichidae
    Polytrichales (*Polytrichum*)

Practical Study

1. Collect several different mosses and study the arrangement of the leaves, mode of branching and the cell types and distribution in the leaves.

2. Cut sections of stems and leaves. This is not as difficult as it sounds. Make a small hole in the centre of some pith and with a pair of forceps push several moss stems into it. Then cut with a razor or razor blade and put the sections directly into a drop of water on a microscope slide.

3. Search for material with capsules. Study their external morphology—use a lens and then a dissecting microscope. Finally cut sections both transversely and longitudinally, as recommended above for transverse sections, and by making a slit in the pith for the longitudinal. Again this is easier than it appears. Crush some other capsules and look at the spores. (N.B. Sectioning of old capsules is difficult and in any case much of the tissue is broken down, so use the younger material.)

4. Slice off the peristome and compress on a slide under a cover-glass. Observe how many peristome teeth there are and distinguish the inner and outer teeth.

5. Attempt to grow the spores on agar or in liquid culture.

6. Design experiments to test the resistance of moss spores to desiccation.

7. Search greenhouse pots, soil surface, etc., for moss protonema. How do you distinguish it from filamentous green algae? Transfer to a moist atmosphere in the laboratory and follow growth of young shoots.

8. Attempt the culture of mosses from fragments of leaf, stem etc.

9. Look for antheridia and archegonia especially in mosses which form a distinct apical rosette.

10. *Sphagnum* is rare in towns! However, leaves and spores can be readily obtained from the *Sphagnum* peat which is used in boxes for growing mustard and cress. Desmids can also sometimes be found in this.

Review Questions

1. What are the distinguishing characteristics of the Bryopsida and the three major sub-groups?

2. How do the Bryopsida differ from the Hepaticopsida. Which group appears the more complex from (*a*) a vegetative and (*b*) a reproductive standpoint.

3. Describe briefly the characteristics of the sporophyte generation. Is this complex structure any more efficient than the simpler capsule of the Hepaticopsida?

4. The moss capsule has reached the height of complexity for a 'parasitic' structure. Discuss what might be the next stage in evolution.

5. Although small plants, Bryophyta must contribute to the natural economy. How and to what extent do you think they do this?

BIBLIOGRAPHY

BOWER, F. O., *Primitive Land Plants—also Known as the Archegoniatae*, Macmillan, London, 1935 (reprinted 1959)

PARIHAR, N. S., *An Introduction to Embryophyta*, Vol. I, *Bryophyta* (4th edn), Central Book Depot, Allahabad, 1961

SMITH, G. M., *Cryptogamic Botany*, Vol. II (2nd edn), McGraw-Hill, New York, 1955

WATSON, E. V., *The Structure and Life of Bryophytes*, Hutchinson, London, 1967

10

INTRODUCTION TO THE VASCULAR LOWER PLANTS AND THE PSILOPHYTA

THE vascular 'lower plants' form a section of the Tracheophyta, which of course includes all plants with conducting systems dominated by the development of tracts of xylem and phloem. However, the 'lower plant' section is clearly distinct even on a vegetative, morphological basis since the apical meristems giving rise to these conducting strands are frequently single cells, or at most a few cells, and only very rarely is there a residual meristem left between the xylem and phloem. This latter feature was more common in some of the fossil groups (see p. 135). In addition, the vascular 'lower plants' have in most instances retained distinct archegonia and antheridia and also a distinct 'alternation of generations', which here is extremely heteromorphic since the sporophyte is a vascular plant and the gametophyte (prothallus) a 'liverwort-like' plant. Of course there are exceptions, but lines of evolution from the Bryophyta and into the Gymnosperm/Angiosperm series can be discerned. These lines are often hypothetical and will remain so until fossil or other evidence is forthcoming—many exciting concepts are undoubtedly emerging as more and more fossils are studied and there is no doubt that biochemical and electron-microscope determined details will assist these. Only further facts will reveal the lines of evolution, but discussion of the *possibilities* will stimulate study of this fascinating group of vascular plants which have a longer fossil history than any other group of vascular plants.

The various groups of 'vascular cryptogams' have traditionally formed the division known as the Pteridophyta, which is broadly based on the fact that the sporophyte in all of them is a photosynthetic vascular plant and this alternates with a relatively minute independent non-vascular gametophyte which may be photosynthetic or nurtured via a mycorrhizal system. Thus the balance of gametophyte and sporophyte is completely the reverse of that in the Bryophyta. However, most modern workers recognize that several quite distinct evolutionary series are involved and these are preferably placed in separate divisions. The term 'pteridophyte' used in an adjectival sense conveys the concept of the whole group as outlined above with the accent on the life-cycle.

The *Psilophyta* are the most primitive, in the sense of least complex, group of vascular plants, and are thus the starting point of any consideration of the development of morphology, anatomy and reproductive structures amongst vascular plants, including Angiosperms. However, the Psilophyta contains two distinct groups—the fossil Psilophytales (*Figure 10.1*) and the extant Psilotales (*Figure 10.2*) which have an extremely restricted distribution. The first peculiarity they have in common is the absence of roots, these being replaced by an underground dichotomizing stem or rhizome-bearing rhizoids for absorption of water, and in the living forms, small scale leaves. In *Horneophyton* this underground structure swells into a series of 'bulbs' (*Figure 10.1 D*). Branches of the rhizome system emerge to form the assimilating stems—naked in *Rhynia*, bearing small scale-like leaves in *Asteroxylon* and *Psilotum* and moderately large laminae in *Tmesipteris* (*Figure 10.2 F*). The anatomy of these structures is only slightly more complex than the most complex conducting systems of Bryophyta such as in *Polytrichum*. The tissues are aerated via stomata, but only in *Tmesipteris* do these occur on the leaf surface. Cortical regions are relatively simple with slight variations in cell form and wall thickening and centrally a simple stele is formed. This consists either of a stellate mass of xylem surrounded by a few rows of simple phloem cells or, in the aerial parts of *Psilotum* and *Tmesipteris*, becoming siphonostelic or even branching to form a primitive actinostele (see *Figure 10.2* for diagrammatic representation of these and other stellar types). The central tissue in the siphonosteles is often sclerified and in the actinostelic type the phloem penetrates in between the bundles of xylem. Endodermal and pericyclic tissues are very indistinct.

Sporangia were merely terminal swellings of the upright branches in *Psilophyton* (*Figure 10.1 E*), whilst in *Psilotum*, trilocular and in *Tmesipteris*, bilocular sporangia are essentially axillary subtended by bifid appendages (*Figure 10.2 A, E*). Superficially the position of the sporangia in the two groups forms a major distinction but there are theories suggesting that the sporangia of the Psilotales are actually born terminally on very reduced axillary branches and indeed in both genera there is a vascular strand passing up towards the base of the sporangia. It has also been proposed that in *Psilotum* the sporangiophore is comparable to that of the Sphenopsida (see p. 139). A spike-like arrangement of sporangia is only found in one genus of the Psilophytales—*Zosterophyllum* (*Figure 10.1 F*), but although this has traditionally been placed here, recent work

Figure 10.1. Psilophytales. *A*, Hornea; *B*, Asteroxylon *plant and C, section through stem showing central actinostele;* *D*, Horneophyton; *E*, Psilophyton; *F*, Zosterophyllum

suggests that it may be one of quite another series of lower plants. Indeed within the next few years it is likely that our concepts of this very simple group of fossils will change greatly as more fossils are investigated. For the present one should think of them as merely a series of examples of very ancient vascular plants.

124

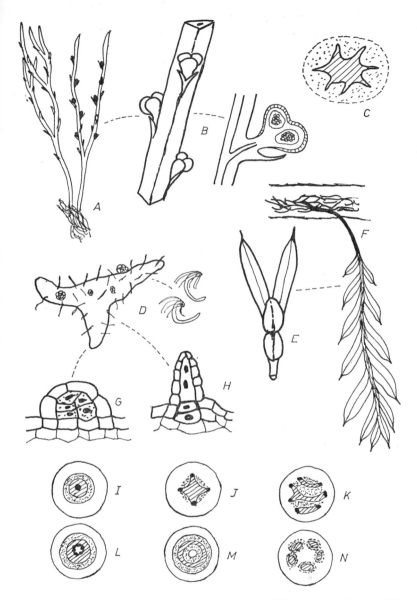

Figure 10.2. Psilotales. A, plant of Psilotum; *B, segment of* Psilotum *stem with sporophylls and trilocular sporangia. On right, a sporangium in section; C, diagram of the actinostele of* Psilotum; *D, prothallus of* Psilotum *and two multiciliate sperm cells; E, bifid sporophyll and bilocular sporangium of* Tmesipteris; *F,* Tmesipteris *plant; G, H, young antheridia and archegonia of Psilotales; I–N, stellar arrangements in the vascular cryptogams. Protoxylem —black, metaxylem—cross-hatched, phloem—dotted; I, protostele; J, actinostele; K, plectostele; L, ectophloic siphonostele; M, amphiphloic siphonostele; N, polystele (individual groups are meristeles)*

Groups of tetraspores can be seen within the fossil sporangia, but gametophytes are unknown. The sporangia do not have any obvious dehiscence mechanism. The kidney-shaped spores of *Psilotum* germinate to form a minute, usually underground, rhizome-like gametophyte. These gametophytes are non-photosynthetic, instead nutrition is via an endophytic fungus. They are also unusual in that a small amount of vascular tissue (both xylem and phloem) is located in the centre of the otherwise parenchymatous thalli. The archegonia and antheridia form in the usual manner from superficial cells and both protrude from the surface (*Figure 10.2 G, H*). The sperm are spirally coiled and multiflagellate. The embryo is exoscopic and in this respect very similar to that of the Bryophyta.

Both sporophyte and gametophyte can bud off gemmae, from the rhizomes in the case of the sporophyte.

Classification

Psilophyta. Sporophytes consisting of rhizomes and stems with or without simple leaf-like enations. Protostelic–siphonostelic. Sporangia without indusia, terminal or axillary. Homosporous. Gametophytes when known, underground with endophytic fungus and slight central vascular tissue, monoecious. Embryo exoscopic.

Two Orders

Psilophytales. Fossil (*Rhynia, Horneophyton, Zosterophyllum, Psilophyton, Asteroxylon, Hornea*)

Psilotales. Living. *Psilotum. P. nudum*, stems triangular. Pantropical. Ground living. *P. flaccidum*. Stems flattened. Isolated in tropics. Epiphytic on trees. *Tmesipteris*. Several species. Epiphytic on tree ferns, etc., but sometimes ground living

Practical Study

This is the most difficult of all groups since you need access to fossil material. If near a large natural history museum you may find displays of fossils and reconstructions. Finding fossils of this group in the field is very much a specialist activity.

Tmesipteris is not easy to obtain and few botanical gardens cultivate it. *Psilotum*, however, can be grown fairly easily although it is not common in collections.

126

Review Questions

1. What are the basic characteristics of the Psilophytales and Psilotales?

2. What are the features which appear to unite these two groups? Do you think this is a reasonable union?

3. How do the Psilopsida differ from the Bryophyta? Are there any features of the latter group which appear to you to be more advanced than corresponding features of the Psilopsida?

4. Survival or otherwise of ancient groups of plants may have been due to catastrophic or gradual extinction. Are there any features of the Psilophytales which might suggest an inability to cope with changing conditions?

5. Assuming that all plant groups have evolved from simpler groups can you conceive of an ancestral type for the Psilophytales? Or may they be simplified or degenerate forms derived from more complex plants?

BIBLIOGRAPHY

BOWER, F. O., *Primitive Land Plants—also Known as the Archegoniatae*, Macmillan, London, 1955 (reprinted 1959)

FOSTER, A. S. and GIFFORD, E. M., *Comparative Morphology of Vascular Plants*, Freeman, San Francisco and London, 1959

PARIHAR, N. S., *An Introduction to Embryophyta*, Vol. II, *Pteridophytes*, Central Book Depot, Allahabad, 1955

SMITH, G. M., *Cryptogamic Botany*, Vol. II (2nd edn), McGraw-Hill, New York, 1955

SPORNE, K. R., *The Morphology of Pteridophytes*, Hutchinson, London, 1962

11

THE LYCOPHYTA

THIS is a compact group of plants with three genera common enough to enable students to study sufficient living material and place the fossil groups into perspective. They are microphyllous plants in which the leaf trace is so slight that its departure from the stele does not affect the latter structure. Three sub-groups clearly emerge at an early stage of study, the first—Lycopodiales—is homosporous with simple spirally arranged leaves, whilst the second—Selaginellales—are heterosporous and have a small structure, the ligule, situated at the base of the upper surface of the leaf, whilst the third—Isoetales—are also heterosporous and ligulate but the leaves are acicular, growing from a bulb-like structure with the youngest leaves in the centre (*Figures 11.1–11.3*).

Homosporous plants (Protolepidodendrales) occurred during the Cambrian, Silurian and Devonian periods and were possibly the forerunners of the genus *Lycopodium*—in fact such genera as *Protolepidodendron* would appear to be only slightly less advanced (*Figure 11.4 A*) than the extant genus. The creeping stems were clothed in bifid microphylls having a distinct vascular trace and some of the upturned branches bore sporangia in the axils or on the upper surfaces of the leaves. A few modern *Lycopodium* species, e.g. *L. selago*, are just as simple, although the leaves are not bifid and roots grow from the axis, often associated with a point of branching (*Figure 11.1 A*). However, in other species—or genera, according to certain workers—the sporophylls are clustered into apical cones where the sporophylls differ in size and shape from the vegetative microphylls and are more closely imbricate (*Figure 11.1 B*), hence the common names 'ground pine' or 'club moss'. Upright, creeping and pendulous (epiphytic and tropical) growth forms occur, sometimes accompanied by anisophylly (unequal development of the leaves—much more common in *Selaginella*, see below). In all Lycopsida the leaves are borne directly on the stems and are often decussate, with a central mesarch vascular trace surrounded by relatively undifferentiated mesophyll. The stem anatomy is distinctly variable, the cortex and stele exhibiting various forms. Some species have actinosteles whilst in others the xylem has fragmented to form

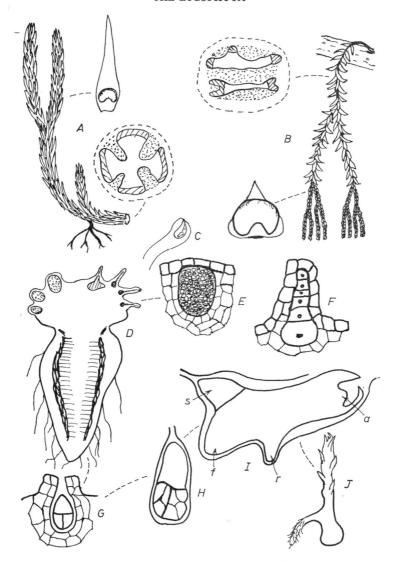

Figure 11.1. Lycopodiales. *A, an upright* Lycopodium *species, sporophyll and transverse section of stele, protoxylem points cross-hatched, metaxylem—white, phloem—dotted; B, an epiphytic* Lycopodium *species, sporophyll and stele; C, biflagellate gamete; D, prothallus with antheridia, archegonia and embryo; E, sunken antheridium; F, protruding archegonia; G, H, I, stages in the development of the embryo, (s) suspensor, (f) foot, (r) root, (a) stem apex; J, young plant*

a series of islands or flat plates in between which the phloem extends. The arrangement of protoxylem is always exarch (*Figure 11.1 A, B*).

The sporangia are characteristically 'kidney-shaped' on a short stalk and often yellow in colour. They are borne on the upper surface of the sporophylls at the base or almost in the axil and curved in the plane of the stem epidermis. Development is of the eusporangiate type (that is from a group of cells) and no particular dehiscence mechanism is developed. The spores are very light (sold as '*Lycopodium* powder'), often ornamented with spines, etc., and pressed into three ridges on one side where they form tetrads.

Germination of the spores leads to the formation of gametophytes (prothalli) which may develop subterraneously and depend on endophytic fungi for nutrition or grow at the soil surface as a cone-shaped structure with photosynthetic lobes spreading at the surface (*Figure 11.1 D*). Antheridia and archegonia are initiated from surface cells and develop in a normal manner, the archegonial necks protruding and the antheridia sunken. The spermatozooids are biflagellate.

The zygote divides first in the plane transverse to the archegonium and the upper cell enlarges to form an organ known as the suspensor, which is an attaching structure. From the basal cell the embryo proper develops and grows laterally through the gametophyte tissue, differentiating to form an apex and first root and between these and the suspensor a foot which anchors the embryo in the gametophyte (*Figure 11.1 G, I*). This type of orientation of the developing embryo is termed endoscopic.

Selaginella also has a range of habit similar to that of *Lycopodium*, but in general the plant is much finer with smaller and often aniso-phyllous (heterophyllous) leaves. These leaves often form two outer ranks of large leaves and two inner ranks of small leaves in a dorsi-ventral arrangement (*Figure 11.2 A, C*). What appear to be roots arise at the branch points of the stem—these are in fact geotropic stem-like structures devoid of leaves and termed rhizophores—the end is swollen and true roots arise endogenously in it (*Figure 11.2 A*). The leaves in section often show a loose mass of parenchyma or even a slight development of palisade tissue. At the base of the leaf in the centre-line is a minute scale (ligule) attached to a bulbous base which fits into a small pit (*Figure 11.2 F*). This organ is at first difficult to observe, but if the leaves are stripped off in a backwards direction it is usually visible. The ligule is also present in the same position in the sporophylls and the sporangia are sited between it and the stem (*Figure 11.2 G*). An interesting feature

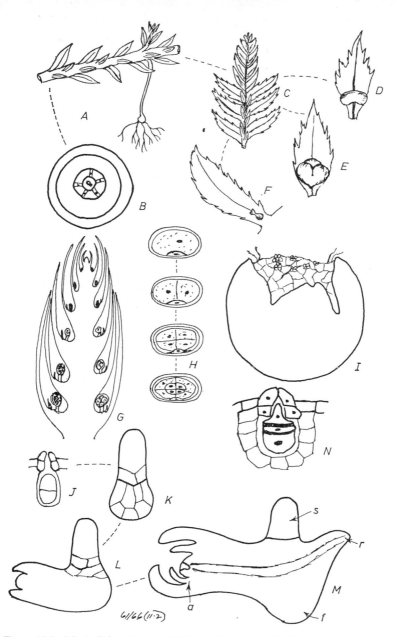

Figure 11.2. Selaginellales. A, part of Selaginella *plant with rhizophore and roots; B, diagram of transverse section of stem with trabecular endodermis supporting the central stele; C, cone at apex of a* Selaginella *plant; D, microsporophyll and microsporangium; E, megasporophyll and megasporangium; F, leaf with ligule at base; G, diagram of longitudinal section of* Selaginella *cone; H, four stages in the development of the microspore into an antheridium; I, a fertile megaspore with archegonia buried in apical tissue; J–M, development of the embryo, (s) suspensor, (r) root, (f) foot, (a) stem apex; N, archegonium*

of the stems, and one which makes the cutting of good hand sections difficult, is the development of a trabecular endodermis supporting the stele in what is virtually a tubular internal air space (*Figure 11.2 B*). The *Casparian* thickenings are quite prominent and one may encircle two or more endodermal cells. The steles themselves are relatively simple protosteles though in many species fragmentation has occurred to give ribbon-shaped and even siphonostelic types. The protoxylem is always exarch and in some species quite distinct vessels occur—this is normally considered an Angiosperm feature although reported elsewhere amongst vascular cryptogams.

The sporophylls are always clustered to form cones and the micro- and megasporangia occur in the axils below the ligules: unlike those of *Lycopodium* they are more nearly spherical or ovoid and the megasporangia often distend into lobes by the swelling of the megaspores. The sporophylls are arranged in four rows equally around the cone axes, which do not show the dorsiventrality of the vegetative shoots. There is, however, often a restriction of the megasporophylls to the base of the cone or, in some dorsiventral species, along the lower side of the cone. In the microsporangium numerous sporocytes undergo meiosis to form a mass of tetrads, but in the megasporangium usually all but one sporocyte abort and hence only four megaspores form—in some sporangia even fewer mature.

Both microspores and megaspores commence development in the parent sporangia and although usually released, in some species the life cycle can be completed with the new plant growing out of the gametophyte whilst this is still retained within the split megaspore in the open megasporangium. The microspore divides within the spore wall to form a single 'prothallial' cell and an antheridial initial cell, i.e. a two-celled gametophyte (*Figure 11.2 H*). The antheridial initial cell divides to form a sterile outer layer or antheridial wall and an inner mass of four cells, each of which divides several times ultimately forming biflagellate sperm cells. The megaspore is much larger and the nucleus first proceeds through a stage of free nuclear division without wall formation. Ultimately walls form around the nuclei in the peripheral zone and the megaspore wall bursts to reveal the cell mass of the female gametophyte. In this exposed region archegonia are formed (*Figure 11.2 I*) and the subsequent development is similar to that of *Lycopodium*.

Isoetes (Quillwort) is aquatic or grows in moist places. The long leaves are organized, as in many water plants, with internal air channels separated by longitudinal septae at right angles to one another and with transverse septae crossing the quadrants at

132

scattered points (*Figure 11.3 A, C*). The basal parts of the leaves are expanded into colourless clasping bases with a prominent ligule at the point between the colourless base and photosynthetic blade. This is perhaps the easiest subject for cutting longitudinal sections through the ligule and its swollen base. Below the ligule are the micro- or megasporangia embedded in the leaf surface (*Figure 11.3 B, D*) and partially covered over by a flap of tissue (velum).

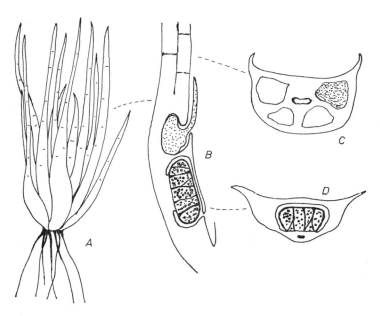

Figure 11.3. Isoetes. *A, plant; B, longitudinal section through sporophyll showing ligule and microsporangium; C, transverse section of leaf with its longitudinal chambers and one cross diaphragm; D, transverse section of microsporophyll in the region of the microsporangium*

The sporangia of *Isoetes* are unusual in that sterile bands of tissue traverse the interior. All the leaves are potentially fertile and megasporangia form in the outer leaves and microsporangia in the inner. The development of the gametophytes is similar to those of *Selaginella* but the spermatozooid is multiflagellate. The leaves arise from a corm which is an enigmatic organ about which much has been written. The shape of its vascular tissue (anchor-like), its secondary thickening and the deeply endogenous origin of the roots are all of interest. It has been likened to the basal stock of the fossil genus *Pleuromeia* (*Figure 11.5 C*). Recently a new genus, *Stylites*, has been discovered in high Andean lakes. The growth of the corm in this genus is even more individualistic, for roots arise on one side only.

The Lepidodendrales and Pleuromeiales are fossil groups of heterosporous/ligulate Lycopsida which in many ways were more complex than the extant genera. *Lepidodendron* and *Sigillaria* were

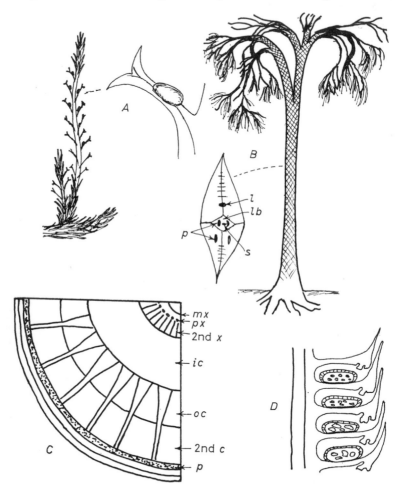

Figure 11.4. Fossil Lycophytes. A, Protolepidodendron *and sporophyll; B, reconstruction of* Lepidodendron *and leaf scar, (l) ligule scar, (lb) leaf base, (p) parichnos, (s) vascular trace; C, part of transverse section of* Lepidodendron *stem, (mx) metaxylem, (px) protoxylem, (2nd x) secondary xylem, (ic) inner cortex, (oc) outer cortex, (2nd c) secondary cortex, (p) phellogen; D,* Lepidostrobus—*longitudinal section of cone—microsporophylls above and megasporophylls below*

quite large trees growing during the Carboniferous period. They are characterized by leaf scars in oblique rows in the former genus and in vertical rows in the latter (*Figures 11.4 B, 11.5 B*). The scars reveal the position of the leaf base (*s*) and also a pit (*l*) directly above the leaf trace which was *impressed upon* the stem by the ligule (*Figure 11.4 B*). Two structures entirely unknown in modern lycopods occur on either side of the leaf trace—these are the parichnos scars (*p*) believed to represent zones of aerating tissue which ran from the cortex into the leaves. There may be two other scars beneath the leaf scar which are also parichnos strands branching off those entering the leaf and appearing on the stem surface below the leaf base. The internal anatomy of these massive stems was extremely variable, but in general there was a relatively small central stele and an extensive cortex. The primary wood consisted of a ring of protoxylem groups surrounding a central tube of xylem or mixed xylem and parenchyma (i.e. the primary xylem was developed towards the centre of the stem—centripetal). The secondary thickening was then formed outside the protoxylem as centrifugal rows of tracheids, thus burying the protoxylem (*Figure 11.4 C*). At the base the stem divided into a series of dichotomizing 'roots' and at the apex into a similar series of dichotomies bearing leaves and terminal cones. The 'roots' or '*Stigmarian* axes' are remarkable structures, bearing the scars of 'rootlets'. These 'rootlets' are similar in internal structure to the roots of *Isoetes* in that the stele was formed along one side of a central 'pith cavity'. The use of the term *Stigmaria* applied to only part of a plant is a feature of palaeo-botany and it is known as a 'form genus'. This arises from the difficulties associated with the description and linking up of separate parts of fossil genera. Rarely are leaf, stem, root, cones, etc., all found together and hence each part is described and named separately (form genera) and gradually as the detective work proceeds these are linked together to give a picture of the plant as a whole.

Leaves were in general simple linear structures with a single leaf trace. The cones were composed of compacted sporophylls as in the modern genus *Selaginella* and often produced into an abaxial lobe which protected the sporangium of the leaf below (*Figure 11.4 D*). The micro- and megasporangia were large and extended some length along the sporophyll.

Sigillaria (*Figure 11.5 A, B*) differs from *Lepidodendron* not only in the vertical rows of leaf bases but also in the unbranched apex, which bears a cluster of long leaves, and in the formation of a ring cluster of cones borne below the region of the leaves and apparently

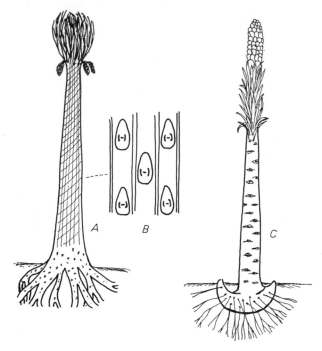

Figure 11.5. Fossil Lycophyta. A, Sigillaria—*note acicular leaves and cones hanging down below leaves; B, arrangement of leaf bases on longitudinally fluted stem; C*, Pleuromeia—*note cone above leaf region and anchor-like basal region*

growing from the stem in a manner analogous to the cauliflorous growth of some Angiosperm trees.

In *Pleuromeia* the axis is again unbranched but a cone of rather plate-like sporophylls terminates the axis (*Figure 11.5 C*). Of greater interest, however, is the massive base with a number of upcurved lobes which have been likened to the 'anchor-like' stelar mass of *Isoetes*.

Classification

There is a very sharp distinction into the eligulate/homosporous and the ligulate/heterosporous series.

Eligulate
    Protolepidodendrales. Fossil (*Protolepidodendron*)

136

Lycopodiales. Fossil and present day (*Lycopodium*)
Ligulate
   Selaginellales. Fossil and present day (*Selaginella*)
   Lepidodendrales. Fossil (*Lepidodendron, Sigillaria, Pleuromeia*)
   Isoetales. Fossil and present day (*Isoetes, Stylites*)

Practical Study

1. In coal mining regions fragments of the fossil forms can sometimes be found in the waste heaps.

2. *Lycopodium, Selaginella* and *Isoetes* are not the easiest plants to
find. In some countries they may be abundant and in others almost
completely absent. Some *Lycopodium* species are distinctly Arctic/
alpine in distribution and are restricted to such regions or to high
altitudes, e.g. in the British Isles. *Isoetes* is not uncommon in acid
water lakes, in moorland or mountain regions. *Selaginella* is more
easily obtained since several species are grown as ornamentals in
greenhouses.

3. Investigate the gross morphology of any material you can
obtain. Look particularly for fertile shoots, origin of roots or rhizophores and arrangement of leaves.

4. Cut transverse sections of stems and leaves. Stain in aniline
chloride (xylem and other lignified tissue stains yellow) or phloroglucinol and hydrochloric acid (stains lignin red). Surface sections
of leaves often reveal a distinct distribution of stomata. Good
transverse sections of *Selaginella* are difficult—the steles tend to drop
out. Note the trabecular endodermis.

5. Section any spore-bearing regions—note thickening of sporangial wall and any indication of lines of dehiscence.

6. Investigate spore structure and attempt to germinate the spores
—growing the gametophytes is difficult since some require endophytic
fungi. The megaspores of *Selaginella* can be attempted on agar.

7. Strip leaves off *Selaginella* and look for ligule. Take the tip of the
leaf with forceps and strip downwards taking a section of the stem
as well. The ligule is often very difficult to see for the first time—it
is small and colourless and one has to focus the microscope down on
to the upper leaf surface.

8. Longitudinal sections of *Selaginella* cones are quite easy to make
and often reveal the ligule in section.

9. If *Isoetes* can be obtained, the ligules and sporangia are much
larger and easier to observe—the ligule is black. Cut transverse and
longitudinal sections of the leaves to see the arrangement of
diaphragms.

10. The morphology of the *Isoetes* root stock is very difficult but worthy of some attempt to section and study.

11. Section any rhizophores and roots and study the stelar structure.

Review Questions

1. Review the basic characteristics of Lycophyta and of the constituent orders. What are the features which unite these into a single division?

2. How were some of the fossil forms more complex than the present day genera? If they were really more complex were they then more efficient? Yet they presumably did not compete well with the surrounding vegetation—why?

3. Discuss briefly the nature of the gametophytes associated with homospory and heterospory. What advantages, if any, does heterospory confer?

4. Is there any obvious similarity between the Lycophyta and the Psilophyta or do they appear to be completely independent groups?

5. The Lycophyta show some of the simplest trends towards the development of fertile cones. What advantages or disadvantages might this incur?

6. How does the form of the leaves correlate with the histology of the stems?

BIBLIOGRAPHY

BOWER, F. O., *Primitive Land Plants—also Known as the Archegoniatae*, Macmillan, London, 1955 (reprinted 1959)

FOSTER, A. S. and GIFFORD, E. M., *Comparative Morphology of Vascular Plants*, Freeman, San Francisco and London, 1959

PARIHAR, N. S., *An Introduction to Embryophyta*, Vol. II, *Pteridophytes*, Central Book Depot, Allahabad, 1955

SMITH, G. M., *Cryptogamic Botany*, Vol. II (2nd edn), McGraw-Hill, New York, 1955

SPORNE, K. R., *The Morphology of Pteridophytes*, Hutchinson, London, 1962

12

THE SPHENOPHYTA

THE age of the Sphenophyta was the Carboniferous, when they formed forests of large trees; today only the solitary genus *Equisetum* remains. They are unmistakable plants with articulated stems organized on a radial pattern, with branches and leaves arising in whorls at the nodes, whilst between are fluted internodes. The sporangiophores are terminal and themselves whorled. The designation Articulatae has been used by some authorities.

One of the most abundant fossils in the group is *Sphenophyllum* and this shows that in the Carboniferous the Sphenophytes had distinct leaves and not the small chaffy scales of *Equisetum*, but even more characteristic are the steles of this genus, with a triangular mass of primary xylem with secondary rays radiating as small cells from the three protoxylem points and larger rows from the areas between (*Figure 12.1 F*). Similar whorled leaves are found in calamitian genera (*Figure 12.4 A*) but the stems were more massive structures arising from articulated underground rhizomes as in the modern *Equisetum*. Since the branching was whorled these tree forms, which grew at the same time as the *Lepidodendrons*, must have been unstable structures. The stems had a large pith cavity, a ring of discrete vascular bundles in the earliest forms but a continuous cylinder in *Calamites* itself. A general characteristic of these fossils and the single present day descendant is the cavity formed around the protoxylem elements and the small amount of primary metaxylem which is produced (*Figures 12.4 B* and *12.2 E*).

Equisetum is a low herb, growing in hedgerows, waste places and also in fresh water. The underground rhizome produces upright branches and also perenating buds. Roots form beneath the chaffy scales at the nodes. Similar scales fused in a ring form the non-photosynthetic leaves of the stems (*Figure 12.2 B*). The photosynthetic tissue is in the cortex of the stem between the thickened epidermis, which has rows of sunken stomata in the grooves, and the conspicuous large cortical canals (vallecular canals) beneath grooves of the stem. The ridges of the stem form the supporting elements with clusters of silicified cells beneath each ridge (*Figure 12.2E*). The vascular strands are relatively inconspicuous and can best be

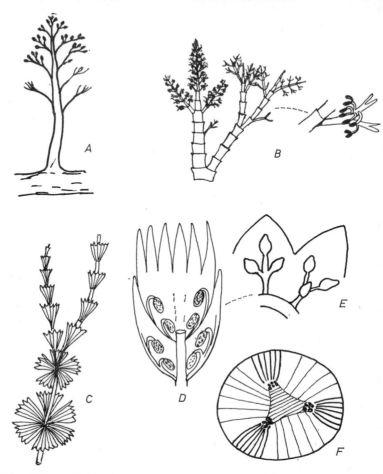

Figure 12.1. Fossil Sphenophyta. A, Protohyenia; *B,* Calamophyton—*part of branch and sporangia; C,* Sphenophyllum; *D, E, part of cone of* Sphenophyllostachys *in longitudinal section and from above; F, stele of* Sphenophyllum. *Primary wood in centre and protoxylem at three corners, secondary wood outside with small cells radiating from corner and larger cells between*

located by looking for the small protoxylem (carinal) canals which occur beneath each rib and between the vallecular canals. Frequently a single protoxylem tracheid can be seen attached to the side of the canal. External to the protoxylem canal the two groups of metaxylem are differentiated with a block of phloem between. An endodermis may surround each bundle or there may be a single

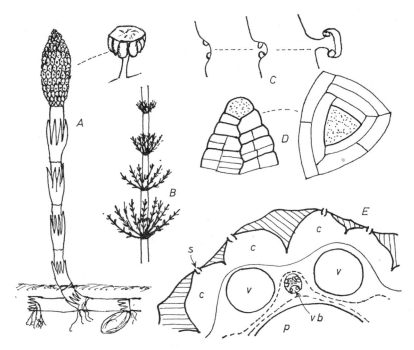

Figure 12.2. Equisetum. *A, part of plant with fertile shoot, single sporophyll on right; B, segment of vegetative shoot; C, origin and growth of sporophylls and sporangia; D, apex in longitudinal section and from above; E, part of transverse section of stem, (s) stoma, (c) chlorophyllose tissue, (v) vallecular canals, (p) pith canal, (vb) vascular bundle, endodermis dotted*

endodermis external to the complete ring of bundles; in some species an internal ring also occurs (*Figure 12.2 E*). A single apical cell with four cutting faces occurs at each stem apex but elongation of the stem is also continued by residual meristems at the base of each internode. Branch primordia are located just above each node between each scale leaf and when they develop they break through the fused leaf bases.

Cones are formed at the apices of the branches of the vegetative shoots or in some species on special non-photosynthetic shoots (*Figure 12.2 A*). The sporangiophores arise as outgrowing bulges on the axis and gradually acquire a peltate form. Between 5 and 10 sporangia are initiated from surface cells and these project inwards towards the cone axis (*Figure 12.2 C*). The spores are released by shrinkage of the sporangiophore and of the cone axis. Each spore is unusual in that the outer spore wall is laid down as four spiral strips of thickening and these act as elators (*Figure 12.3 A*)—they coil round the spore when moist and uncoil as the surface dries.

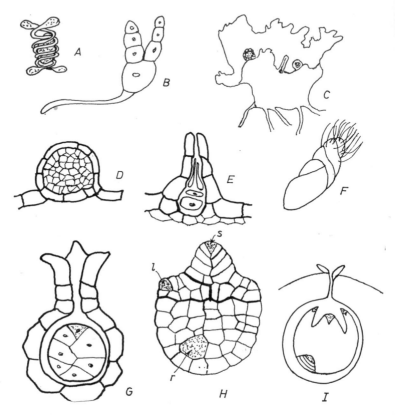

Figure 12.3. Equisetum. *A, spore with elators wound around it; B, young prothallus; C, prothallus with antheridia and archegonia; D, antheridium; E, archegonium; F, coiled and multiciliate spermatozooid; G, H, I, stages in the development of the embryo, (s) stem, (l) leaf, (r) root*

Within the Sphenophyta a range of sporophyll types can be traced from the branched apical form of *Protohyenia* through *Calamophyton, Sphenophyllostachys, Calamostachys* to the modern *Equisetum* type (*Figures 12.1* and *12.4*).

The spores germinate and form small thalloid, lobed photosynthetic gametophytes on which both antheridia and archegonia are formed (*Figure 12.3 B, C*). The spermatozooids are coiled and multiflagellate. Development of the embryo is exoscopic with the formation of a foot which anchors the embryo in the gametophyte tissue (*Figure 12.3 G–I*).

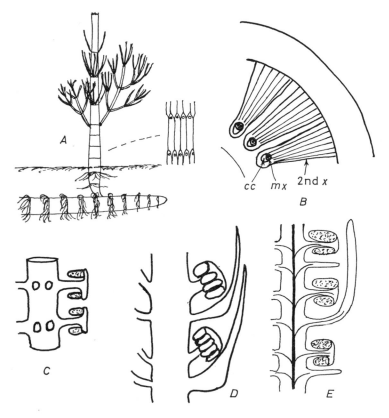

Figure 12.4. Calamitales. A, Calamites, *and on right part of the stem; B, transverse section of Calamitian stem showing carinal canal (cc), metaxylem (mx) and secondary xylem (2nd x); C, part of the cone of* Asterocalamites; *D,* Palaeostachys; *E,* Calamostachys

Classification

Hyeniales. Fossil (*Protohyenia, Calamophyton*)
Sphenophyllales. Fossil (*Sphenophyllum, Sphenophyllostachys*)
Calamitales. Fossil. Small trees (*Calamites, Calamostachys*)
Equisetales. Fossil and extant Herbaceous (*Equisetum*)

143

Practical Study

1. Stems of 'calamite' fossils are quite common on some waste heaps at coal mines. They are recognized by the ribbing of the stem crossed by the lines at which the leaf/branch system arose at the nodes.

2. Note the external whorled morphology of a modern *Equisetum*. Determine the arrangement of leaves at successive nodes and of the rib system between. Look for stomata by cutting surface longitudinal sections or stripping the epidermis off. What is unusual about these stomata?

3. Investigate the anatomy of an *Equisetum* plant. The stems are often difficult to section owing to the thickened sub-epidermal tissues. Stain with aniline chloride or phloroglucinol to see the very slight xylem elements.

4. If material can be found with immature cones, these can be sectioned transversely and longitudinally and the development of the sporophylls traced.

5. Mature cones can be dissected to see the arrangement of the sporangia. Are the sporangial walls thickened and is there a line of dehiscence?

6. Put some spores on a microscope slide. Breathe on them and watch the movements of the elators under the microscope. What effect is breathing on them having?

7. Germinate some spores on agar or on damp soil and attempt to grow the gametophytes.

Review Questions

1. Why do the Sphenophyta rank as a division of the 'pteridophyte' series?

2. How does the morphology of the modern *Equisetum* compare with the fossil forms?

3. Are there any possible indications why this group has been relatively unsuccessful? What might be the reasons for the success of *Equisetum*?

4. What other 'articulate' groups of 'lower plants' are there? How successful are they and how do they compare with the Sphenophyta?

5. Compare the Sphenophyta with Lycophyta and Filicophyta. How do the spore-bearing structures differ in the three divisions?

BIBLIOGRAPHY

BOWER, F. O., *Primitive Land Plants—also Known as the Archegoniatae,* Macmillan, London, 1955 (reprinted 1959)

FOSTER, A. S. and GIFFORD, E. M., *Comparative Morphology of Vascular Plants,* Freeman, San Francisco and London, 1959

PARIHAR, N. S., *An Introduction to Embryophyta,* Vol. II, *Pteridophytes,* Central Book Depot, Allahabad, 1955

SMITH, G. M., *Cryptogamic Botany,* Vol. II (2nd edn), McGraw-Hill, New York, 1955

SPORNE, K. R., *The Morphology of Pteridophytes,* Hutchinson, London, 1962

13

THE FILICOPHYTA—FERNS

THIS is by far the most complex group of vascular Cryptogams. The contribution of the fossil and living forms is here reversed since there are a very large number of modern genera of ferns and only a few fossils. Although world-wide in distribution there are distinctly more genera and they are more conspicuous in the vegetation in moist tropical regions, particularly in the southern hemisphere. In the previous groups the leaves were relatively small structures (microphylls) and their vascular traces were so slight that the stelar systems of the stems were hardly modified by their departure. The Filicophyta on the other hand have large leaves (megaphylls or macrophylls) relative to the stems and the leaf traces are massive enough to leave gaps (leaf gaps) in the main stelar system when they depart. A further characteristic of the megaphylls is their circinate (coiled) vernation in bud and their fairly extensive apical growth. These leaves are generally considered to be branch systems which have flattened and developed mesophyll tissue as webbing between the branches. If this is indeed the correct interpretation then it is not surprising that the leaf gaps are more prominent than in the microphyllous forms since they are really 'branch gaps'. In the positioning of the sporangia it has already been demonstrated that in the microphyllous genera the earliest fossil forms had a distinct tendency to form sporangia at the apices of the branches. This is also a characteristic of primitive ferns, but whereas in the microphyllous types the tendency was one of transition to the axil or upper surface of the leaf—a natural enough sequence if one regards this as a reduction of a branch system plus an associated microphyllous outgrowth—in the macrophyllous ferns the leaf probably developed by growth of tissues between the branches (webbing) and below the sporangia, and hence the original position of the sporangia would be on the leaf margin and the natural sequence would then be displacement on to the leaf surface. It so happens that in almost all cases this movement to the surface position occurred in such a way that the sporangia in modern ferns lie on the undersurface of the leaf (abaxial). The sporangia themselves are much more delicate structures in the genera of the Filicales living

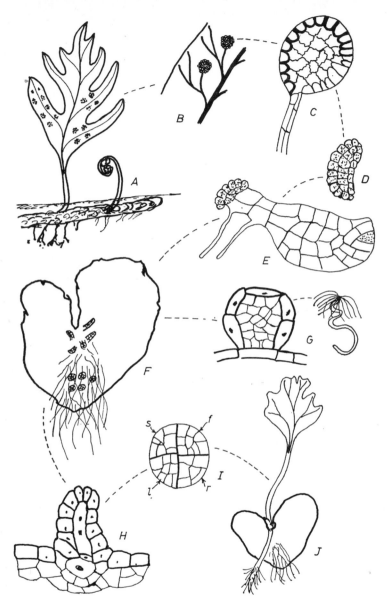

Figure 13.1. Life cycle of a fern. A, Polypodium *plant; B, naked sori on the back of the leaf; C, sporangium; D, spore; E, young prothallus growing from the spore; F, prothallus from underside with archegonia and antheridia; G, antheridium and spermatozooid; H, archegonium; I, young embryo, (s) stem, (f) foot, (r) root, (l) leaf; J, young plant still attached to the prothallus*

today compared with fossil and relict groups. A protective structure, the indusium, appears in this section alone of the vascular cryptogams. A representative fern (except the indusium) and the stages of the life cycle are shown in *Figure 13.1*.

Four groups of ferns are recognized by most authorities (see p. 159), of which the Primofilices are entirely fossil and the other three have both fossil and living genera. The bulk of genera are classified in the Leptosporangidae.

Primofilicidae

This sub-class contains some plants which appear very similar to the microphyllous fossils, e.g. *Cladoxylon* with its fan-shaped leaves and terminal sporangia (*Figure 13.2 A*), but it already possessed a complex stele. Really recognizable fern-like foliage is found in *Etapteris* although it is unusual in that the petiole branches at the base giving rise to two pinnate leaves lying in almost the same plane (*Figure 13.2 B*). Both vegetative and fertile fronds occur and in the latter the leaf segments have been modified to form massive sporangia, each with a distinct annulus. In this as in many other Primofilices the vasculation of the petioles was complex (*Figure 13.2 C*) and probably more so than in most modern ferns.

Eusporangidae

The eusporangiate ferns, i.e. those in which the sporangia originate from a group of cells, form a very small group with a few living genera and some fossils. Only a small number of ferns have retained separate vegetative and reproductive fronds and the Ophioglossales are considered the most primitive of these. The small stem remains underground or in epiphytic species buried in leaf bases, etc., after growth from the tuberous gametophyte. Usually only one leaf is produced each year and emerges without any trace of circinate vernation. In *Ophioglossum* ('Adders Tongue') it is entire, but in *Botrychium* ('Moonwort') it is simply pinnate (*Figure 13.2 E* and *G*). In both genera the fertile spikes arise as bifurcations at the base of the vegetative lamina. In *Ophioglossum* the sporangia are fused into two rows along the upper third of the spike (*Figure 13.2 F*). Much has been written concerning the interpretation of the spike but it is now generally thought that it is basically two pinnae fused together. The sporangia of *Botrychium* are not fused and are borne along a pinnate fertile spike as though they were replacing the laminae which occasionally recurs in some species (*Figure 13.2 H*).

In the tropical Marattiales the rather coarse, massive pinnate

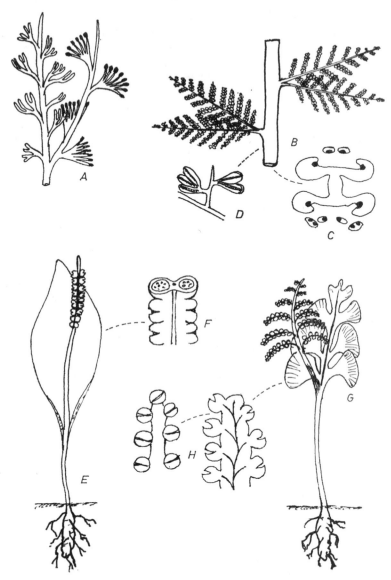

Figure 13.2. Fossil ferns and Ophioglossales. A, Cladoxylon, *vegetative and fertile shoots;* B, Etapteris—*vegetative branch;* C, *stele of* Etapteris *petiole with lateral bundles. Black areas are protoxylem points;* D, *sporangia of* Etapteris; E, Ophioglossum; F, *part of fertile spike of* Ophioglossum; G, Botrychium; H, *fertile spike and section on right*

leaves often have swollen bases (pulvini) and stipules and arise from short upright axes up to 1 m in height (*Figure 13.3 A*). The stelar system of these short axes is complex, often a series of concentric

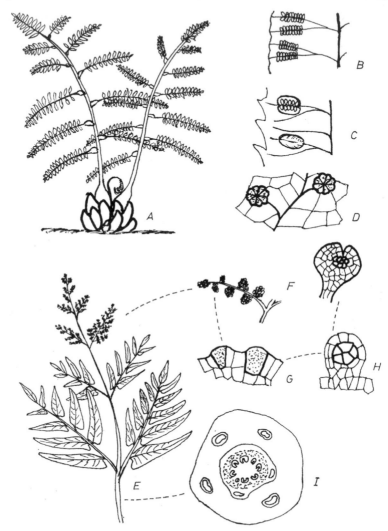

Figure 13.3. Marattiales and Osmundales. A, Angiopteris. *Note swollen base of pinnae; B, synangia of* Angiopteris; *C,* Marratia; *D,* Christensenia; *E,* Osmunda; *F, fertile segment and sporangium with plate-like annulus; G, two forms of sporangial initial cells; H, later stage of sporangium; I, transverse section of* Osmunda *stele with U-shaped xylem strands and external phloem*

rings of meristeles (see p. 125). The sporangia are massive structures borne in clusters along the veins on the lower surfaces of the leaves (*Angiopteris*) or fused to form a series of synangia in the other genera (*Marattia, Danea* and *Christensenia*) (*Figure 13.3 B–D*). The sporangial walls are massive and unusual in the possession of stomata. There is no well defined annulus—the sporangia merely split as the walls dry.

A small group intermediate between the Eusporangidae and the Leptosporangidae has long been recognized as the Osmundidae (Protoleptosporangiatae—is another rather inelegant term for the group). They are a good example of a relict group of plants with a long fossil history. *Osmunda* has a short upright stem bearing pinnate leaves (*Figure 13.3 E*). The anatomy of the stem is complex with a ring of U-shaped xylem strands with the protoxylem in a mesarch position at the base of the U and external to these xylem strands is a complete ring of phloem (*Figure 13.3 I*). Some of the fronds bear scattered sporangia on the under surface of the leaves but the main fertile fronds have the laminae almost completely reduced and the sporangia are formed in a marginal position (*Figure 13.3 F*). There is no indusium and the massive sporangia are short-stalked with an 'annular' patch of cells on one side—dehiscence occurs through a slit passing from this 'annulus' over the top of the sporangium. The sporangia arise from single cells but these are variable in form (*Figure 13.3 G–H*).

Leptosporangidae

Three orders are generally recognized—Filicales, comprising all the remaining land ferns, and the two small orders of Leptosporangiate water ferns, Salviniales and Marsileales. The life history is exactly that outlined in the introduction to the vascular cryptogams but the large number of genera necessitates further discussion.

The spores of the Filicales vary greatly in size and shape from spherical to kidney-shaped, with an outer layer usually sculptured (*Figure 13.1 D*). In germination the outer wall splits and the gametophyte grows out as a filament which gradually divides to form a flat plate of photosynthetic cells—the prothallus or gametophyte. In the Hymenophyllaceae, however, the filamentous stage is prolonged and branching occurs to give an algal-like prothallus. The parenchymatous type differentiates an apical cell which cuts off cells laterally so that a bi-winged structure forms (*Figure 13.1 F*). Single-celled rhizoids form at a very early stage but later become aggregated down the centre line. In most gametophytes the centre becomes more than one cell thick and in a few (e.g. *Gleichenia,*

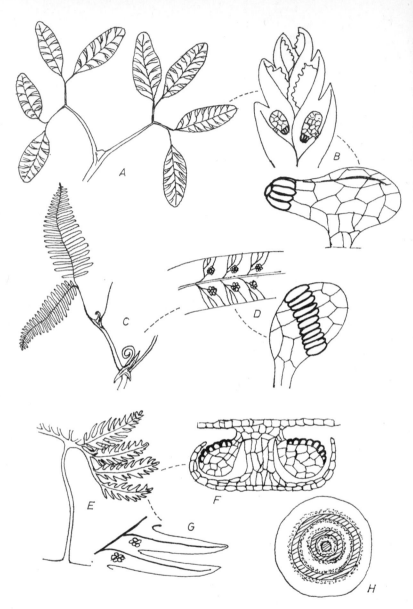

Figure 13.4. Leptosporangidae. A, Lygodium; *B, solitary sporangia covered by leaf flaps and below, a single sporangium with a terminal annulus; C*, Gleichenia; *D, naked sori and single sporangium with oblique annulus; E*, Matonia; *F, massive sporangia covered by indusium; G, sporangia on leaf with indusium removed; H, polycyclic steles of* Matonia, *xylem—striate, phloem—dotted*

Figure 13.4 C) the whole thallus becomes multilayered. Endophytic fungal invasion of some swollen cells of the filamentous gametophyte tissue is recorded in the Schizaeaceae. Vegetative propagation of the gametophyte from gemma-like outgrowths is common in some genera and in a few these even become thickened and act as perennating organs. Archegonia and antheridia are normally found in the central thicker tissue on the undersurface. In the Hymenophyllaceae they form on small multicellular pads growing from the filaments. Although the gametophyte is a dorsiventral structure there is no histological dorsiventrality except for the production of rhizoids, and early workers showed that inverting the gametophytes resulted in rhizoids and gametangia on the upper surface. They assumed that gametangia were initiated on the shaded side.

The zygote divides to form a quadrant stage (*Figure 13.1 I*) and from the sectors the first stem, root, leaf and foot are formed, but until more species are studied it cannot be said how precise the embryogeny is in relation to the primary division of the zygote. The gametophytic tissue proliferates to some extent to form a rather indistinct calyptra protecting the embryo. The first leaves are generally simple (*Figure 13.1 J*) and resemble a dichotomous branching vascular system with webbing of mesophyll tissue between the branches, i.e. a primitive state.

Development of sporophytic plants on fern gametophytes without fusion of sperm with egg is recorded for many species—this is known as apogamy and the resulting plant may be haploid or diploid if the gametophyte is diploid as a result of apospory, see p. 157).

Two main growth forms characterize the sporophytic stage of ferns. Radial organization is best illustrated by the tropical tree ferns, e.g. *Dicksonia* or *Alsophila* in which there is a distinct stem up to several metres high. Some radial ferns have very short axes, e.g. *Dryopteris* or *Blechnum* spp., but can be recognized by the spiral cluster of leaves apparently rising out of the soil. The other and even commoner type is the dorsiventral, creeping rhizomatous type, e.g. *Pteridium* ('Bracken') or *Polypodium* (*Figure 13.1 A*) in which the fronds arise in an alternate sequence. Anatomically there is a considerable range and no single description will fit the Filicales— in *Gleichenia* the stele is a rod of xylem with parenchyma intermingled amongst the tracheids and surrounded by a complete ring of phloem, i.e. protostelic, in *Dennstaedtia* the stele is tubular and siphonostelic, with phloem and endodermis both externally and internally, whilst concentric siphonosteles are found in *Matonia* (*Figure 13.4 H*). If the rhizome of *Dennstaedtia* is sectioned at the point of origin of a leaf trace then the stelar ring is seen to be broken at one point. When these breaks, so-called leaf gaps, are extended longitudinally up the stele and overlap one another the stele then appears as a ring of separate vascular bundles, e.g. *Pteridium*. These have metaxylem in the centre, are surrounded by phloem and each is termed a meristele; the complete stelar system is dictyostelic (polystelic—*Figure 10.2*). If the entire stelar system is dissected out it would be found to consist of a much divided cylinder and *not* a series of separate tubes. At the stem apex is a three-sided apical cell—also present in the roots but cutting off additional cells parallel to the outer face to form the root cap. Roots are mainly adventitious and usually have diarch xylem with two groups of phloem on either side and a very thickened inner cortex. In many ferns and particularly the tree ferns the stem is clothed with old roots which have arisen from the base of the leaves and it is these which form the supporting tissue.

The leaves ('fronds') are initiated in the surface tissue a short distance behind the three-sided apical cell of the stem (rhizome) and are recognizable as biconvex lens-shaped cells. The apical meristem of the leaf is persistent and hence the fern leaf undergoes a long period of apical growth (up to three years in some species) which is in distinct contrast to the rather limited growth of Angiosperm leaves. Development of the leaf lamina is dependent upon the existence of marginal meristematic cells—thus the growth of ferns is traceable to a series of apical cells at the apices of the vascular system, as would be expected if the organization is basically a branching stem system. The mature leaf is differentiated into a lower petiole and upper rachis bearing the finer branches with wing-like laminae ('pinnules'). Some ferns are climbing plants and the leaves grow relatively little, but the rachis continues the growth, e.g. the tropical genera *Lygodium* and *Gleichenia* (*Figure 13.4, A, C*). The lamina functions as the major photosynthetic organ of the plant and also bears the sporangia. Occasionally the two functions are somewhat separated, e.g. in *Blechnum* where the laminae bearing sporangia are much reduced. A few tropical epiphytes exhibit anisophylly—for example, some leaves are modified to form flattened expanses growing against the host trunk, *Platycerium* (*Figure 13.5 E*).

The laminae of fern leaves are constructed on a dorsiventral plan as in the Angiosperms. The stomata tend to be confined to the under surface whilst palisade and mesophyll tissue is developed to varying degrees. The vascular traces of the petiole are often complex and in the form of a U-shape which is sometimes broken up into meristeles. Two other characteristics of fern leaves are the circinate vernation and the occurrence of fine hairs or scales (ramentum) on the

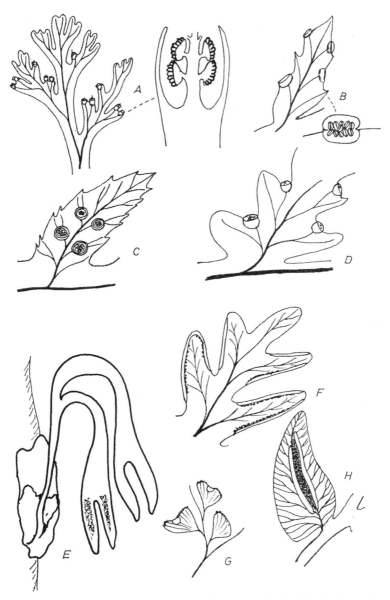

Figure 13.5. Leptosporangidae. A, Hymenophyllum, *fertile leaf and longitudinal section through the sorus; B*, Dicksonia, *with two-lipped indusium; C*, Cyathea; *D*, Dennstaedtia; *E*, Platycerium—*dimorphic leaves; F*, Pteridium; *G*, Adiantum; *H*, Blechnum

155

epidermis. Circinate vernation is the inrolling of the rachis in a radial plane accompanied by inrolling of the branches in a plane at right angles to that of the rachis (*Figure 13.1 A*). The ramentum of ferns is very variable, ranging from simple hairs to thin 'leaf-like' chaffy scales and is abundant in the young stages, particularly on the petiole but sometimes extending on to the leaf surface.

Sporangia are formed from single surface cells at precise positions on the under surface of the leaf. A short filament of cells is formed by growth from an apical cell which then cuts off internal segments to form the sporogenous initials and the nutritive tapetum. The sporangial wall is one cell thick and the lower tiers of the initial filament elongate to form a usually thin stalk. The sporangial head has a cluster or ring of thickened cells (annulus) which acts as the dehiscence mechanism working on a weaker region of unthickened cells (stomium) (*Figure 13.1 C*). The sporangial head is shaped like a biconvex lens with the annulus around the periphery and the stomium adjacent to the stalk—this is the common form in the majority of Leptosporangiate ferns classified in the large artificial family Polypodiaceae. A series of supposedly less advanced families have the annuli running obliquely round the sporangia, which tend to be more pear-shaped, and this series culminates (or starts) in the family Schizaeaceae with a plate-like annulus (*Figure 13.4 B*).

In all genera the sporangia are clustered into groups (sori) and in a few genera these are completely unprotected, e.g. *Polypodium* (*Figure 13.1 B*), and often slightly sunken in the leaf tissue although when mature the sporangia project as yellowish-brown patches. Naked sporangia also occur in *Gleichenia* (*Figure 13.4 D*) and *Dipteris*. By far the larger number of genera have the sporangia raised slightly on a receptacle and covered, especially during early growth, by a flap of tissue called the indusium. Sometimes this grows from the centre of the receptacle (*Polystichum*) and sometimes from one side (*Asplenium*) or from both sides (*Scolopendrium*). In a few genera the receptacle is elongated and even grows from a basal meristem (Hymenophyllaceae, *Figure 13.5 A*) whilst at the base it is protected by a two-lipped indusium. In *Cyathea* a much shorter receptacle in a superficial position is surrounded by a cup-shaped indusium (*Figure 13.5 C*). A further modification in the Schizaeaceae is that the massive sporangia are hardly grouped and a flap of tissue covers each one (*Figure 13.4 B*) or the leaf edge incurves over the sporangia. Many trends have been defined relating to the original and present-day position of the sori, e.g. from a marginal (Hymenophyllaceae), to superficial position (Cyatheaceae), from separate to confluent sori (*Pteridium*) to separate again. There is also a range in the order of development of sporangia—in some ferns all the sporangia mature at the same time (simple or Simplices, e.g. *Gleichenia*) in others the sporangia mature in succession (gradate—or Gradatae, common amongst ferns with elongate receptacles, e.g. Hymeno-phyllaceae) and finally, and regarded as the most advanced stage, others mature in any order in the sorus (mixed—or Mixtae, e.g. *Pteridium* and almost all Polypodiaceae).

Apospory has been recorded in a few ferns—in this the leaf or the sorus gives rise to diploid prothallial tissue on which antheridia and archegonia develop. Fusion of the gametes results in tetraploid plants.

Vegetative propagation also occurs, e.g. in the commonly grown *Asplenium bulbiferum* which is often seen in greenhouses with small plants growing out of the frond midribs.

In addition to the Filicales there are two further small orders of aquatic ferns in the Leptosporangiate group. They are unusual for ferns in being heterosporous with the gametophytes developing within the spore and therefore atypical for the ferns as a whole. The Marsileales grow rooted in bogs or standing water and produce dichotomously branched rhizomes—leaves are formed and in *Pilularia* they are 'grass-like', whilst in *Marsilea* they are of a 'four-leaved clover' form (*Figure 13.6 A, B*)—they are circinately rolled in bud and those of *Marsilea* undergo nyctinastic movements. The rhizomes have air spaces in the cortex—a characteristic of many aquatic plants. The *Salviniales*, on the other hand, are floating aquatics with short branching stems lying along the water surface giving rise to leaves which spread out over the water surface. In *Salvinia* there is an under-row of leaves which are dissected and give the impression of roots (*Figure 13.6 I*)—true roots occur only in the genus *Azolla* (*Figure 13.6 H*). Cavities in *Azolla* leaves contain an endophytic blue-green alga *Anabaena azollae*.

The sporangia are borne in capsules (known as sporocarps) formed from modified leaves and in the Marsileales these are hardened to form nut-like structures. There has been considerable discussion and speculation concerning the origin and development of these structures, particularly in the Marsileales. In *Marsilea* the sporocarps are paired on short stalks growing out from near the base of the pinnules (*Figure 13.6 B*) whilst in *Salvinia* they form at the base of the divided underwater leaves and in *Azolla* on the lower lobes of the first leaves of side branches. In the Marsileales the sporocarp consists essentially of two halves forming a nut, inside which a mucilage thread runs circumferentially bearing a double row of alternate sac-like sori (*Figure 13.6 C*). In each sac is an

M   157

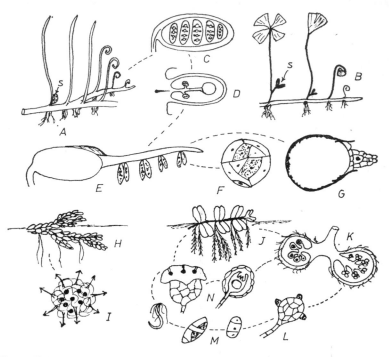

Figure 13.6. Water ferns. A, Pilularia, *linear leaves and sporocarp* (*s*); *B*, Marsilea—
sporocarp (*s*); *C*, *longitudinal section through* Marsilea *with five sori in the sporocarp; D,
sorus of* Marsilea *in transverse section with terminal megasporangium and lateral microsporangia; E, dehiscing sporocarp with sori hanging on mucilaginous thread; F, germination
of microspore to form two antheridia and single male prothallial cell; G, female gametophyte
with single archegonium; H,* Azolla; *I, massula of* Azolla *with microspores and hooked
glochidia; J,* Salvinia; *K, section through sporocarp with megasporangia and microsporangia;
L, microsporangium with germinating microspores penetrating the wall; M, developing
microspores and spermatozooid; N, megasporangium on right and forming prothallial tissue
with archegonia on left*

elongate receptacle on which sporangia develop in a 'gradate'
manner. The upper develop into megasporangia and the lower into
microsporangia (*Figure 13.6 D*). Only one spore develops in the
megasporangium whereas all spores in the microsporangia are
fertile. The microspore cuts off one prothallial cell and then a series
of cleavages define two antheridia surrounded by a few wall cells
(*Figure 13.6 F*). The megaspores are larger and have an apical bulge
in which a few cell divisions occur whilst the bulk of the megaspore
remains filled with cytoplasm. The divisions in this apical region
form a single archegonium (*Figure 13.6 G*).

The sporocarps in *Salvinia* consist of an outer wall (probably a modified indusium) enclosing a receptacle which either bears a small number of short stalked megasporangia or a larger number of longer stalked microsporangia (*Figure 13.6 K*). The microspores germinate within the microsporangia (*Figure 13.6 L*) and push through small openings in the wall. Development is similar to that in *Marsilea*. The microspores in *Azolla* occur in groups in the microsporangium surrounded by an alveolar plasmodium which in some species develops hooked processes (glochidia)—the whole structure is termed a massula (*Figure 13.4 I*). The microspores germinate within the massula.

Classification

The term Filicophyta for the division containing all the ferns is one which has been used by palaeobotanists and avoids the problem of using the older terms (e.g. Pteridophyta sensu stricta, Pteropsida, etc.) which have had such various usages.

Primofilicidae (Primofilices)
  Cladoxylales (*Cladoxylon*)
  Coenopteridales (*Etapteris*)

Eusporangidae (Eusporangiatae is usually quoted even in Engler's, 1954 Syllabus, but -idae is the correct ending for a sub-class)
  Ophioglossales (*Ophioglossum, Botrychium*)
  Marattiales (*Marattia, Danea, Angiopteris, Christensenia*)
Osmundidae
  Osmundales (*Osmunda*)

Leptosporangidae
  Filicales. This is a large order containing almost all the ferns and it is better subdivided into families
    Schizaeaceae. Tropical. Some climbing ferns. Sporangia massive—solitary (*Lygodium*)
    Gleicheniaceae. Tropical. Climbing or scrambling. Sporangia massive in sori (*Gleichenia*)
    Matoniaceae. Tropical. Rhizomatous. Sporangia massive— umbrella-shaped indusium. Polycyclic stele (*Matonia*)
    Dipteridaceae. Tropical (*Dipteris*)
    Hymenophyllaceae. Mainly tropical, a few temperate. Filmy ferns. Gradate marginal sorus (*Hymenophyllum*)
    Dicksoniaceae. Tropical tree ferns, sori marginal (*Dicksonia*)

159

Cyatheaceae. Tropical tree ferns. Sori superficial with or without cup-shaped indusia (*Alsophila, Cyathea*)

Polypodiaceae. World-wide. Sori abaxial or marginal. Indusia varied or absent. A massive group split into many sub-sections (*Dennstaedtia, Davallia, Pteridium, Polystichum, Polypodium, Scolopendrium, Blechnum, Dryopteris, Platycerium, Adiantum*)

Marsileales. (*Marsilea, Pilularia*)

Salviniales. (*Salvinia, Azolla*)

Practical Study

Fortunately ferns are generally available and the Leptosporangiate type is basically so similar throughout that study of any genus gives the essential details of the group. There is no virtue in searching for a particular type, e.g. *Pteridium* just because it is the commonly illustrated form in many textbooks.

1. Collect and study the general vegetative morphology of a few ferns. Distinguish between radial and rhizomatous types.

2. Section stem, or rhizome, which is often smaller and therefore simpler, and note the arrangement of tissues. Stain in the usual way. Section the pinnules and compare their internal structure with that of an Angiosperm.

3. Use a dissecting microscope to determine the form of the indusia. Note also the relationship of the sori to the underlying vascular system. Attempt to section through the sori—thin sections are not essential.

4. Scrape off some young and old sporangia and determine their structure.

5. Look for prothalli and young plants either around older plants in their natural habitat or more easily on the soil or staging around ferns in a greenhouse.

6. Remove some spores from old sporangia and illustrate their form. Note particularly the arrangement of the annulus and stomium on the sporangia.

7. Attempt to germinate the spores in the laboratory on agar or on sterilized soil.

8. Spread spores on to soil or fragments of plant pots in the greenhouse. Cover with glass and keep moist. One technique often used is to up-end a plant pot full of peat into a tray kept full of water and sprinkle spores over the pot—enclose under a bell jar and prothalli should develop.

9. Search the prothalli for archegonia and antheridia and illustrate the structure of these. They are relatively easy to find.

10. Dissect out any young plants from the prothalli and compare their leaf form with that of mature ferns.

Review Questions

1. Review the distinguishing characteristics of the Filicophyta.

2. What features have the Filicophyta in common with other vascular cryptogams and how do they differ?

3. Trace the changes in sporangial form throughout the four sub-classes. Is there any apparent increase in efficiency of spore production and mechanism for dispersal?

4. Discuss the ways in which the sporangia are aggregated on the leaf surface. Why are they clustered, has it any biological advantages?

5. The indusium is often a very delicate filmy flap of tissue. What purpose does it serve? How do some 'polypodiaceous' ferns cope without it?

6. The gametophyte of ferns appears to be morphologically a much less variable structure than the sporophyte. Is this really so?

7. Only in very specialized habitats have ferns succeeded in becoming dominant in the vegetation. What are these habitats and why are ferns more successful here than elsewhere?

8. How does the morphology of the vascular system compare with that of the Lycophyta on the one hand and the Gymnosperm/Angiosperm series on the other hand?

BIBLIOGRAPHY

BOWER, F. O., *Primitive Land Plants—also known as the Archegoniatae*, Macmillan, London, 1935 (reprinted 1959)

BOWER, F. O., *The Ferns*, Vols. 1–3, Cambridge University Press, London, 1923, 1926, 1928

FOSTER, A. S. and GIFFORD, E. M., *Comparative Morphology of Vascular Plants*, Freeman, San Francisco and London, 1959

PARIHAR, N. S., *An Introduction to Embryophyta*, Vol. II, *Pteridophytes*, Central Book Depot, Allahabad, 1955

SMITH, G. M., *Cryptogamic Botany*, Vol. II (2nd edn), McGraw-Hill, New York, 1955

SPORNE, K. R., *The Morphology of Pteridophytes*, Hutchinson, London, 1962

INDEX

163

165